CULTURAL
IMAGES
OF
HEALTH

A NEGLECTED
DIMENSION

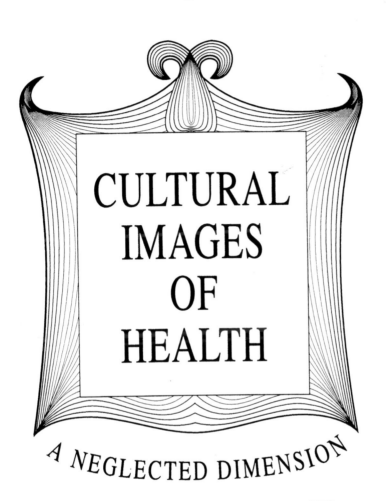

CULTURAL IMAGES OF HEALTH

A NEGLECTED DIMENSION

Alphonse d'Houtaud
and Mark G. Field

NOVA SCIENCE PUBLISHERS, INC.

Art Director: Christopher Concannon
Graphics: Elenor Kallberg and Maria Ester Hawrys
Manuscript Coordinator: Roseann Pena
Book Production: Tammy Sauter, Benjamin Fung
and Michelle Lalo
Circulation: Irene Kwartiroff and Annette Hellinger

*Library of Congress Cataloging–in–Publication Data
available upon request*

ISBN 1-56072-228-2

© *1995 Nova Science Publishers, Inc.*
6080 Jericho Turnpike, Suite 207
Commack, New York 11725
Tele. 516-499-3103 Fax 516-499-3146
E Mail Novasci1@aol.com

Printed in the United States of America

CONTENTS

PART II: CULTURAL IMAGES OF HEALTH

PART III: HEALTH REPRESENTED BY ITS SYMBOLS
AND ANALOGIES

PART IV: HEALTH AND SOCIETY: SOCIO-ECONOMIC REFLECTIONS

Introduction

Cultural Images of Health: A Neglected Dimension

The Problem

The center of gravity of this book is health, not illness. Its purpose is to help address and redress a long neglected aspect of our studies of health and health care systems. In most instances, concern about health is, in fact, concern about illness. Although we do not speak of a World Sickness Organization or of a Ministry of Public Illness, this is precisely what is meant in most instances, in spite of the World Health Organization's grandiose statement about health not being simply the absence of disease, but a state of complete physical, mental and social well-being. Most of medical sociology, and medical anthropology for that matter, focus on pathology, morbidity, trauma and less than optimal life-expectancy.

This book attempts to reverse this perspective by emphasizing the meaning, the significance and the importance of health in contemporary industrial and urban society. It offers the English-reading public some of the pioneering work done on the subject in France in the last two decades, a work that is well-anchored in the Durkheimian tradition i.e., the notion of collective representations: the ideas, concepts, clichés, stereotypes and conventional wisdoms that people carry around in their heads, share with each other and transmit to their children. These representations are not simply images: they have consequences for individual and collective comportment. In fact what they do is that they order, they organize, they systematize the outside world of those who hold them. They provide meanings, orientation, a kind of cognitive map of the environment.

And in the case that concerns us here these representations are centered on the question of health, what it means, what one should do to maintain it, preserve and protect it; and also most important where and how to seek help when health it threatened, and to whom to turn. It is thus important to have also a better image of the institutions society has established and maintained to help those who seek health care. It thus places health at the center of preoccupations, and not as a function of illness and in the shadow of medical institutions and medical models.

It should be added that representations are cultural concepts, usually learned by the individual in the process of socialization, and modified to some extent by life experiences and cultural changes. Their substantive contents tend to be specific to the particular national and class milieu in which individuals live, and also tend to vary with such factors as age, sex, and education, as well as income and geographical location, among others. They are by no means universal or uniform, just in the same way as health practices do vary from place to place and from time to time. Representations, as a generic phenomenon, are on the other hand to be found in all human cultures and societies. Furthermore this book also presents a discussion of the "functional" role of health in the social system, given its strategic significance for "capacity" and for social role performance. This discussion is then followed by an examination of some of the major issues concerning the health system, conceived as the social response to the threat of illness, both at the individual, clinical level, and at the collective or societal scale.

The subject of this book is important at a time when so much concern attaches to morbidity and premature mortality, and the ever mounting costs of sickness-care. It is therefore critical to have a more accurate idea of what people think of their health as this will necessarily determine what they will do to preserve it (and that of their children) when it is threatened by illness, trauma or impending death. Whether a person will pray, go to healer, visit a physician or treat himself (or do a combination of these) will depend, to a large extent, on his or her concepts of health, on his or her "representations of health". This book not only emphasizes the relevance of the subject: it details some significant and pioneering work done in France and largely unknown to the English-reading public. This work, based on large and representative samples of the population, relates health representations to several socio-economic and cultural variables (age, sex, education, and class position, for example). Thus, among higher socio-economic groups (professionals, managers) health has a definitely *expressive* meaning: it is essential to the enjoyment of life. Among lower socio-economic groups (manual workers, agricultural laborers) health has a specific *instrumental* dimension: it makes it possible to earn a living, and to carry out the orders and directions of managers and professionals.

The reversal of the perspective mentioned earlier (the emphasis on health rather than illness) should weigh heavily in the mounting of future investigations, as well as on the orientation of policies genuinely recentered on health.

Finally, it is hoped that this book will serve as an invitation to English-reading scholars to turn their attention to this area of research, and to make contributions that will permit international collaborative research and meaningful comparative analyses.

This book is the result of the cooperation of two health sociologists with different but complementary orientations. They have been working together for the last ten years, particularly in bringing the work of Dr. d'Houtaud, of Nancy, to the attention of the English-reading public which usually does not have access to French publications. Professor Field is well-known for his pioneering work on Soviet health care and comparative health care systems. His latest book is one he edited with Marilynn Rosenthal and Irene Butter, *Political Dynamics of Physician Manpower Policy* (Elsevier, 1990). Dr. d'Houtaud is a pioneer in the study of health representations as well as that of the image of health professionals. His latest work is a monograph *Comment l'alcoolique se perçoit et se croit perçu* (Riom, 1988). Drs. Field and d'Houtaud have completed two books which appeared in 1989 *Les représentations de la santé: bilan actuel, nouveaux développements* (INSERM) and *La santé: approche sociologique de ses représentations et de ses fonctions dans la société* (Presses Universitaires de Nancy). The present work is an attempt to present, in an English version, a revised, updated and somewhat shortened version of *La santé,* and includes some materials not available in the French book.

PART I

AT THE HISTORIC AND SEMANTICS ROOTS OF THE TERM "HEALTH"

Introduction

1. The Problem

It would be difficult, nowadays, to proceed to a psycho-sociological study of the question of health without, first, looking into the historic and semantic roots of the term and of the concept. Without going into great detail, and though we do not claim any special expertise of the past and of linguistics, we should like nevertheless to present here, with some modifications, the gist of two papers we published about a decade ago (1978 b and 1979). This in order to throw a bit of preliminary light on the history and the semantics of the notion of health.

There is one fundamental question, with such general implications that only multidisciplinary research groups can approach it meaningfully, and that is the following: what are the distant origins of the notion of health and its evolution in the course of centuries in different semantic fields and in diverse cultural areas of mankind and on the entire surface of the globe? In other words, what are the most archaic and the most recent connotations of health in:

- our languages
- in the institutions of our societies
- in the deep structures of our psyches?

2. Object of the Present Study

Our contribution to this vast territory of knowledge is meant to be quite modest and strictly delineated. It will be an approach to the language of health within the restricted framework of Western culture insofar as it is derived from its Greco-Latin origins. Starting with data that have been particularly impressive, we shall propose some reflections or ideas that may be helpful in a historic and semantic understanding of the concept of health.

We shall deal, in chapter 1, with representations of health as expressed in salutations and greetings.

In chapter 2 we shall examine the links between health and religious salvation.

Having done this, we shall attempt to throw some more precise light on the implications of health in individual and collective mentalities that our subsequent empirical investigations will try to illustrate and elaborate. We shall thus endeavor to offer a glimpse of all the enrichment that a psycho-sociological investigation can derive from resorting to the past of a culture.

3. Language as an Institution

We shall deal with language as an institution that permits the individual to communicate with others. Indeed, in order to express his personal thoughts, with all their particularities and all their nuances, each speaker, according to his earlier experience, must select from the immense reservoir of terms and expressions available in his language. It is in that reservoir that the experience of the past generations has been accumulated and condensed. Each domain contains a mass of appellations, of conventional wisdoms or formulations, even picturesque turns of phrases, dicta, clichés, etc. And the domain of health provides us precisely with the fundamental elements to discover its psychosocial origins.

We can only hope that other researchers will add their own contribution to such a vast subject, and eventually will modify or correct our propositions, or at any rate will complement them.

Chapter 1

Health in Salutations

1. When the Ancient Greeks Made a Goddess of Health

Whoever has discovered, in Epidaurus on the Saronic gulf, the best preserved Greek theater of antiquity, is no less surprised by the size of the neighboring archeological site. It, in fact, drew more attention among the ancient Greeks than the theater itself, because it was the sanctuary of Aesclepios, a god whom the Romans called Esculapus. Epidaurus had become as much a place of treatment as of cult, just as was the case, in Asia Minor, of Pergamon, where the cult of Aesclepios was imported from Greece. If we believe Greek legends, this son of Apollo (god of light, healer and purifier) and of the nymph Coronis was such a brilliant medical student of the centaurus Chiron and such an efficient practitioner (did he not, it was said, resuscitate the dead?) that, on the complaint of Hades, Zeus (Apolo's father) had him thunderstruck.

A family of Greek physicians pretended to descend from him, the Aesclepiads they were distant forerunners of modern medical associations and, just like them, very clever in defending their rights and privileges: the Aesclepiads formed a kind of priestly fraternity, very jealous of its secrets, transmitted from father to son. In this double way, Greek mythology and history already strike us by the representations they formulated about health practitioners.

Fortunately, Greek legend does not stop with the failure of thunderstruck Aesclepios, since his daughter, **Hygiea**, remained alive. Popular piety made her the goddess of health. She thus combined a deified feminine personage of health with the cult of the physician-god, who does not have the right any more to vanquish death and who, by divine decree, is defeated by it in his own person. This testifies to a certain ambiguous need, to an irreducible unity, either between sickness and health, or between life and death.

In brief, **Aesclepios** represents the first type of Promethean effort that tends to *destroy that ultimate frontier of life that is death*. Thus it challenges the pre-established order of the fatal sequence of life and death. He is then also the type of hero surviving beyond death through a lineage of disciples. They, in turn, resign themselves to the fate of humans, thanks to the cult rendered to their eponymous ancestor, at the same time victorious and vanquished (*victor vinctus*) by death.

There remains the gracious personalization of **health** that has become the divinized daughter of Aesclepios. She symbolizes *the permanence of health* beyond the death of the god-physician: if an assurance of immortality or of a durable resurrection is absent, health still remains the tangible object of aspirations and human expectations, the *smiling and seducing image of happiness in an ephemereal life*.

Nevertheless, this agreeable vision of life does not prevent pilgrims from going with fervor and with offerings to the ever more prosperous sanctuary of Epidauraus and to its even more numerous branches in Greece, to solicit from *Aesclepios* protection and healing. This lasted until his replacement, in the IVth and Vth centuries of our era, by the healing saints of a predominant Christianity.

One should note, nevertheless, that the Protestant Reformation did distance itself from healing saints, as from the traditions of popular medicine (that of healers, of those who made invocations and who often resisted it). On the other hand, according to R. Bastide (1971), it is necessary to distinguish the attitudes of the Reformed Church toward saints and its attitudes toward healers and herbalists.

2. Health in the Greek Vocabulary

In the Greek language, health already appears in the verb **hugiainô**, which means first *to be well*, to be in good health, simultaneously for individuals, for things, for a country or for an institution; the opposite term **noséô**, *to be ill*, has the same variety of applications. Both are equally used for the mind. The first then also means to recover health, to come back to health, and even to be cured. Let us also note the salutation formula *hygiainé*: keep well. The adjective *hugiès* follows the verb in the multiplicity of its meanings. On the other hand, the noun *hugiéia* adds to good health, then to cure, two interesting meanings: a sort of cake for sacrifices, the medicine itself.

Without a common root with the preceding terms, the verb **sozô** can signify to save in the sense of sheltering from danger, of not killing, of safeguarding, of not losing: a derivative sense is that of conserving, to keep (something) in one's memory. The substantive **sôteria** signifies *salvation*, preservation or conservation.

3. Health in the Latin Vocabulary

In a partially parallel way, Latinity has retained around **sanus** a variety of meanings, comparable to those mentioned earlier regarding the Greek world. Particulary, the same duality of words is used to designate the physical and the mental: thus the *sanior* designates the wiser one; the one who has good common sense is designated by a superlative *sanissimus*. The expression *sana mente* means reasonable, just like *saniter*, whereas *male sanus* refers to the one who is unbalanced; *sanitas* sometimes means reason, common sense. A political regime that operates well is a *sana res publica*. In the active sense, there is the verb **sanare**: to cure someone or a sickness and, more generally, to repair, to remedy.

Another root that veered toward health, **valeo**, from which comes *valetudo*, as much to express the good as the bad state: clearly more the latter in such terms as *valetudinarium* (infirmary, hospital) and *valetudinarius* (the patient). In English the expression *valetudinarian*, which has a positive meaning, derives from it. The verb, however, derives from the meaning of being strong, to be vigorous, to be powerful (this sense expresses itself fully in the adjective *validus*, in English *valid*, which signifies: robust, vigorous, powerful, efficient and in good health) and thus to have value in a race, in wrestling, through arms, to win in a trial because of having friends. Symbolically, one encounters meanings of the following type: to maintain oneself, to have value in speaking of money; then to have significance in speaking of words; and, at last, and particularly for us, to feel well, to be in a good health, from which diverse expressions derive: *vale or valete* (good-bye) to salute, *cura ut valeas* (take care of your health), to end a letter.

The ritual of salutation orients us naturally toward another Latin root: **salus**. This designates the health of the body; and, by derivation, health in the sense of conservation, and finally the act of saluting, the salutation. And from there the adjective *salutaris*. It explains one of the two meanings of **salutare**, that of the *salutem alicui efficere* (to accomplish salvation), then the substantive *salutatio*, which designates the salutation in the sense of greeting and which explains the other meaning of **salutare**, that of *salutem alicui dicere* (to say: hello).

In a parallel way to the second sense of *salutare*, the verb **salvere** comes from *salve, salvete*. It means first to greet someone, then to be in good health, to feel well. And hence the adverb *salve*, in good health, in good shape and the adjective *salvus*, feeling well, well conserved or safe (and is said of the State, of the army, of the traveler upon his return, of the letter sent to its destination, of duty accomplished, etc.).

4. The French Terminology of Health

To express health itself (**santé**), the French vocabulary draws principally on Latin. Among the exceptions the most important one is the term **hygiène** of Greek origin, as is also the case in English. It designates the totality of principles and practices that tend to preserve and to ameliorate health: for example, body hygiene, mental hygiene, public hygiene, although in English the tendency now is to use health, as in mental or public health.

Whether it is a question of the adjective healthy (in French *sain*) or of the substantive health (*santé*), one discovers, as one does in the Greco-Latin terminology, a literal and a symbolic meaning. In the literal sense, healthy designates on one hand the quality of what is intact, unaltered, the good physiological state and on the other the regular and harmonious functioning of the human organism for an appreciable amount of time (independently of anomalies and traumas that do not affect vital functions: in this sense, an amputee, a blind person could be said to be healthy). The state of health thus represents a functioning over a rather long period of time. Inversely, one uses the term unhealthy (*malsain*) for what is sickly, morbid, unsalubrious, rotten, and even for what is impure, immoral: unhealthy waters, unhealthy climate, unhealthy influence. This last example brings us to the symbolic applied to mental life: mental health, intellectual health, a healthy spirit, a healthy judgment, a healthy emotion; or in social life: a healthy business, a healthy management. And so is the English meaning of *sanity* (healthy spirit, common sense) or of *insane* (crazy, deranged, nonsensical). Or in Spanish of *insano* or in French of *insanité*. In a broader sense, one speaks of fragile health or of solid health. One even says "bursting with health".

5. Wishes of Health in the Formulation of Salutations

The terminology of health has brought us to consider several times the **etymological roots common to salutation and to health**. Why is there such a frequent association in Latin languages?

First of all, **salutations** or **greetings** represent, from the socio-psychological perspective, *ritual words* just like good-byes or farewells: there is, indeed, rituals of access as there are rituals of parting. Erving Goffman (1973) has emphasized that the former mark a transition toward an augmentation of mutual access and the latter toward a diminution of such access: he has called them ritual parentheses that enclose an overload of common activity, punctuation signs of a sort. This applies to the *encounter* on the street or at home, to a *letter* or to a telephone conversation. Terms tied to greetings are more frequently associated with access rituals, to the point that one sometimes designates those as salutations; they are also found in the endings of letters. And if the terms do not always exist specifically to introduce access, one finds them implied in the common *how are you?* or *how do you do?* which signifies practically: that I am in the position to meet with you, to carry a conversation with you.

Among Semitic people, salutations usually refer to peace (*shalom*), among the Greeks to joy (*chaïré:* rejoice), among the Latins to health (*salus*), just as in the Old German where **hails** means *healthy* and *salutation* at the same time. This is the same, by the way, in English as *hail*. Among the Semites and the Greeks letters of correspondence or supplications addressed to the king or to the supreme authority were accompanied by wishes of good health. Hittites even had the custom to indicate at the beginning of their letters that they were in good health before formulating wishes of health to their correspondents. In the Roman Empire and among the people subjected to their cultural influence, it was customary, in a statement, to follow the address with a greeting, followed in turn by a term of affection, of benediction. Even the French Revolution, which had eliminated former formulas of civility maintained the word in the expression **salut et fraternité** (greetings and fraternity) at the end of personal letters.

The presence of **wishes in salutations** has become so ritualized that many people, using the language as it is, without ever analyzing it, are not even aware of it. Nevertheless, it is significant, if not of an individual expression, at any rate of a *collective thought somewhat crystallized in the words and in the expressions* of the tradition. Whether it is a question of health, of joy or of peace, the persistence of such wishes in the verbal ritual, and not its disappearance in the course of centuries, expresses well that it is always a matter of the latent preoccupations of people.

On the first of the year, after *happy new year*, one adds *good health*. It is a wish that one proffers also in raising one's glass to the health of someone. To the person who just sneezed, we say: *to your health* or, using the German, Gesundheit! Individuals, in using such standard formulations, contribute to transmit their signification, even if they are not aware of it: this can be verified in other places than in salutations, in particular in swear-words. Through individual speech, it is the group or the linguistic community that transmits the most profound meaning and testifies to the most common tendencies and expectations. Just like gestures, ritual words are carriers of a more fundamental meaning than the obvious sense that their users have in mind.

There are **salutations or greetings by gestures without words**. The doffing of the hat or the hand at the head: originally, it was a question of lowering the visor of a helmet, gesture by which one put oneself at the mercy of someone else. The military salute is a very rigorously organized code: artillerymen salute with a salvo of shells; sailors in furling their sails or lowering their pavillion. At the arrival of a chief of state, a detachment symbolically does the honors by presenting their arms or shoots blank shells, according to a determined number and cadence. The *salutations of arms* is a very ancient politeness before the assault. Let us mention two gestures of salutation: to give the hand to someone you meet, or give him or her a kiss on the cheek (the latter a French custom less usual in Anglo-Saxon circles).

We shall return to the profound significance of the data we have just mentioned in this chapter 1, as well as those we shall mention in the next chapter 2 which is its continuation, when we shall recapitulate Part I. Chapters 1 and 2 constitute an interlinked whole.

Chapter 2

From Salvation to Health

Several times, when in chapter 1 we examined the question of Greco-Latin terminology concerning health and salutations, we saw the issue of salvation emerging: the site of Epidauraus as a place of *cure* and of *cult*, the Greek word *sôzô* and the Latin word of *salus* leading to the idea of the savior, the old German *hails* signifying healthy and salvation.

The question then arises even more powerfully: **what relationship is there, from the historic and linguistic viewpoints, between health and religious salvation?**

1. The Emergence of Oriental Religions of Salvation in the Roman Empire

The same Greek verb *sôzô* and the substantive *sôteria*, which is derived from it, means preservation from danger and salvation by a savior in the lay sense of the word.

Similarly the same Latin root around the verb *salvere* has drifted toward notions of health and salutations, as we have already seen, but equally toward that of religious salvation (the religious savior is *sôtèr* in Greek and *salvator* in Latin).

In other words, behind the parallelism of the two evolutions, terminological and semantic, there is a linguistic diversity introduced by a series of historic events.

These historic events came from Asia in the Hellenistic period: "the propagation of Oriental cults is, with the development of neo-Platonism, the central fact of the moral history of the pagan empire", wrote the historian Franz Cumont in his fundamental work: *Les religions orientales dans le paganisme romain* (1929). It is a work where he examines the religious problem of salvation in the Roman Empire, using a general evolutionary perspective.

Nevertheless, this Hellenistic origin of a religion of mystery, which spread the notion of preoccupation with salvation, was not accompanied by a semantic rapprochement between the Greek terms of health and salvation, nor around the *hygiainô*, nor around that of *sôzô*.

"The essential fact, if one considers the Roman Empire, is that oriental religions spread, before and then in parallel with Christianity, doctrines that have acquired, along with it (Christianity) a universal authority at the decline of the ancient world. The preachings of Asiatic priests also prepared, in spite of them, the triumph of the Church and this triumph has marked the completion of the work of which they were the unconscious architects...".

"And as we study more closely the religious history of the Empire, the triumph of the Church will appear, we think, more and more as the achievement of the end-result of a long evolution of beliefs. One can understand the Christianity of the Vth century, its greatness, its spiritual heights and its childish superstitions, if one knows the moral antecedents of the world where it blossomed... Perhaps the credulity of their (Oriental pagan cults) mysticism deserves all the criticisms to which the liturgy of neo-Platonism has been subjected, and which draws from the same inspirational sources; but, just like it, in affirming the divine essence of the soul, they have strengthened in man the sentiment of his eminent dignity; in making of his internal purification the principal object of his earthly existence, they have refined and exalted public life and have given it an almost supernatural intensity that, earlier, the antic world had not known".

2. The Judeo-Christian Vision of Salvation

If Christianity, according to F. Cumont, owes a great deal to the Asiatic religions of salvation, there is no doubt that it owes much more to one of the most prestigious among them: ancient Judaism.

Many episodes of its more than one-thousand years history evoke salvation in memorable survivals, sometimes ritually evoked: Isaiah promised deliverance during the siege of Jerusalem by Sennacherib; earlier, during the Exodus, the Hebrews were saved from the servitude imposed by the pharaos; in the immemorial tales of Genesis, Noah was saved from the deluge. Other prestigious names signify saved by God (Joshua, Isaiah, Elijah, Samson, Hoseah) or designated saviors (Saul, Samuel, Gideon, Samson, Jesus).

All these themes are defined and found in the texts of the New Testament. At their center the figure of Jesus dominates, whose name signifies Yahveh saves. He is presented as the savior par excellence, since he identifies himself with the salvation, coming through him, of the believers who consider themselves, in turn, saved by him. For Paul of Tarsus, salvation is equally meant for the pagans: salvation which, obtained on this earth in hope, will be given in full at the end of time.

Such a sober presentation of the Christian doctrine of salvation, strictly in accordance with the texts themselves, has only brought out the biblical essentials. These have become obscured and complicated by the multiple additions coming from mystery cults mentioned earlier. Some authors have not hesitated to speak of a syncretism, accomplished by Christianity, starting from these other religions of salvation that came from the Orient into the Roman Empire at the same time.

Nevertheless, this Hellenistic origin of mystery religions, which spread out the notion and the preoccupation of salvation, did not translate itself into a semantic rapprochement between the Greek terms of health and salvation, neither around *hugiainô* nor around sôzô.

3. Three Meanings in One Term (Latin and Germanic)

By contrast, the association of the two meanings of **health** and **salvation** (in the religious sense) in the same term shows, relative to the **Greeks**, an originality of the **Latins** who did not hesitate to use the current and banal word *salus* to express the salvation of sects born in Asia in the area of Hellenistic hegemony; in the **koinè** (the Greek language spoken in the Hellenistic and Roman times), the Asiatic salvation has been translated by the term *sôtéria*, to which we will shortly return. And this originality in the Greco-Latin universe has had, later on, an equivalent in the **Germanic** languages. In fact, the Gotic is an oriental branch of the Germanic languages and designates the language of the Goths, the spelling of the adjective Gothic being different from the substantive.

Where the Latin used the two terms of *sacer* and *sanctus*, the Gotic *hails* carries a double meaning of:-

saint, in the sense of the sacred (in Greek: *hagios*),

and *healthy* in the sense of intact, of physical integrity (in Greek: *hugiès*; in German: *heilen*; or in English: *heal*).

E. Benveniste (1969) continues (t.1 page 187): "From the Gotic *hails* 'in good health, the one who enjoys his physical integrity', has also the function of a form of wish, translating the Greek *Khairé* (salutation). This explains that physical integrity possesses such a characteristically religious value. The one who possesses good health, i.e. who has an intact corporal quality, is also capable to confer good health. 'To be intact' is the good luck or fate one wishes, the omen one expects. It is thus natural that in this perfect 'integrity' or 'wholeness' one can see a sign of divine grace, a sacred meaning. Divinity possesses naturally the gift that is integrity, salvation, good fortune, and it can impart it to men, in the form of bodily health and predicted good luck".

In a parallel way, the English language uses the two terms of **whole** and **holy** in the same way as the double meaning of **hails** in old German.

In German and in English, as in Greek and Latin, the three meanings of health, of salutation and of religious salvation are encountered in one or two terms:

- in Greek: *hughianô* (to save), *hugiès* (physical integrity), *hagios* (saint);
- in Latin: *salvere* (to save), *sacer* (healthy), *sanctus* (saint), *salus* (religious salvation and salutation), *salvator* (savior, saver),
- in German: *heilen* (to cure), *heilig* (saint), *heil* (healthy), *hails* (salutation),
- in English: *whole, holy, hail.*

Nevertheless, only the Latin root *salvere* and the German root *heilen* bring together explicitly the three meanings of health, salutation and religious salvation.

4. From Health to Salvation

Between the two social representations of salvation and health, a certain parallelism emerges on the basis of the following hypothesis: the same term, employed in the languages of Indo-European origins to designate a temporal reality and a reality of the beyond, cannot but affect each other, albeit at the level of the unconscious or of the preconscious of the speakers. Unless it be the expression of a deeper psycho-somatic relationship, real or perceived as such.

Beyond the deep differences that exist between salvation and health, one can discern certain striking analogies. In the two cases, it is a question of a life to safeguard, even to develop. What the liturgy of the initiated is to salvation in mystery religions, the rituals of hygiene have become to health, particularly in the more and more populous cities, usually exposed to epidemics and other nuisances that threaten life. For certain categories of individuals, such preoccupations with hygiene become as absorbing, almost as exclusive, as are the sacred rituals for certain of the converted (there are those persons who are so scrupulous as to become obsessed in the two cases). Salvation must lead, in the beyond, to an eternal beatitude that is complete: and is health not often presented in our civilization as a condition of access to happiness, at least as an element of the quality of life?

Rites of salvation require the mediations of a sacerdotal body, possessing theological knowledge and sacremental power that separates it from the rest of the population. To sacrifice means to sacralize, and **sacerdos** designates the one who accomplishes the sacred; he must not have anything in common with the world of men. By the same token, health also requires a medical corps with a privileged social status, with a prestige that is often envied but rarely equalled. The knowledge of doctors of medicine remains too often as esoteric and obscure as that of doctors in theology. The latter is concerned with the mysterious, with what is hidden.

The two powers are almost free of social controls, each one in its own domain. Worship activities and medical activities are "hunting preserves" on their respective territories. In one case, the approach to the soul, in the other to the body, concerns strict individual intimacy.

What sin is to salvation, illness is to health: in the two domains one meets the specter of death, the culpabilization, the recovery of purity or of asepsis as the absence of infection.

In serious situations, the priest and the physician deploy, in parallel, their respective activities to the same unfortunate, with the participation or the active complicity of the familial and social milieu: as if the patient had, depending on the outcome, always something to console himself with, either with his recovered health, or with salvation as compensation after the purifying phase of the illness. In any case, the duel between life and death concerns the temporal or eternal destiny. The two categories of actors around the patient are not necessarily in a competitive relationship: the physician-believer or the religious person, who treats, cooperates with the minister of the cult around the individual to be saved. For, in this case, for him, salvation comes through his sufferings, even through the sacrifice of his health or of his present life. This in view of the happy life reserved for those who have successfully managed this difficult passage.

Did not Ivan Illich in his *Medical Nemesis* (1975) denounce medical clericalism? His work aims at defending the health of the laity against medical-clerks, as J. Bauderot has explained (1976).

Whatever similitudes and divergences between the two scenarios that we just evoked, we should mention what have been the decisive contributions of religions of salvation to health.

5. From Salvation to Health

The most tangible contribution of religions of salvation has been to displace the center of gravity in that these religions aim less at cementing the individual in society than at validating each one as a person, whose dignity and rights have been progressively recognized in civil and religious legislation. The result is that individual health is not simply an element or factor of growth or expansion of an enterprise or of the national economy. The concern shown, for almost two millenia, in the salvation of all individuals has contributed a great deal to *prepare mentalities to welcome requests for individual health* for itself, sometimes even at the expense of large financial investments. For *each individual health is unique*: all life depends on it in its quality as well as in its longevity. If health is precious to the individual, it is also for those who love him, thus creating around him a network of solidarities and providing him with additional reasons to live as long and as well as possible.

Undoubtedly, the reproach made to salvation religions is of having diverted the attention of individuals from their only tangible possession, their *temporal health*, to the benefit of an unverifiable hope: their *eternal salvation*. Even if these religions have effectively, in short term, *alienated* the human subject by distracting him effectively from concern with his health in favor of that of his salvation, at least they have, in doing so, actually contributed, in the long range, *to prepare the minds and the mentalities for an actual preoccupation, often exclusive, with health*, since they have elevated individuals to the rank of human persons. In giving value to salvation at the detriment of health, they have lifted the individual to such a level that, afterward, the valuation of health has taken place among personal values, and sometimes substituted itself for the former one.

At any rate, in our times, the situation has profoundly changed. In a world less and less attracted by religious beliefs and practices, the clergy, on its own, tends to abandon its medieval status and its sacred isolation and to integrate itself in society, to work there as much for justice on earth as for eternal salvation.

From that point on, the *dangers to individual health* are not to be sought in religions of salvation: they reside, from now on, *in economic powers*, whether public or private, that manifestly profit from it, often exploit it exaggeratedly, sometimes sacrifice it openly for their "bottom lines" and through surreptitiously harmful or subtly illusory products.

6. Health as a Transcultural Value

The other important contribution of the religions of salvation is that, by disengaging the individual religious life from the supervision of the State, to tie it to *universal values*, superior to the material requirements of industrial societies, it has instituted the principle of transcendence which, little by little, has spread to other values. Precisely health, in the measure to which it is essentially what is valuable for each person, and without which the rest does not matter for him, has become one of the transcendental values, if not the most eminent value, at least the most fundamental in individual life (in the sense of the Latin *valere* as mentioned earlier).

Indeed, health, by contrast with the individual of whom it is an irrevocable attribute, could not remain a prisoner in a closed cultural universe, nor the servant of the socio-economic order too often divinized.

From this point on, why not raise and locate the *value of health*, like that of individuals, beyond the socio-cultural framework where it is deployed more and more? In other words, why should the value of health not be recognized universally as *transcultural*? One of the common goods of all individuals and all peoples, to be promoted at the level of humanity?

7. Health in Individual Consciousness and in the Collective Unconscious

With the Latin word *salus*, and around the Germanic root *heil* and its Gotic antecedent *hails*, the triple association of health, salutations and religious salvation was found twice in the Indo-European languages from which depend, to a large extent, our Western civilizations.

The history of these three realities indicates that, beyond the semantic conjunction of the vocables, they were frequently interdependent.

Nevertheless, in our days, we speak and we conform to the usual practices in these three domains without perceiving all that binds them together. It is thus likely that, if the connections do not manifest themselves at the level of the *conscious* strata of our personalities, they exert nonetheless a persistent influence at the more archaic levels of the *subconscious* or the *unconscious*. At least at the level of that type of the **collective unconscious**, that constitutes the *institutions* and the social *practices* that regulate health behaviors, salutations and religious salvation, many connections or analogies testify to the permanence of which that particular social institution that is *language* continues to be a witness.

Assuredly, such historical and semantic associations do not constitute an obstacle to the movement of **secularization** that characterizes our modern times and which is confirmed in the areas of the school and communications media in as patent a manner as in socio-medical institutions.

In reality, the succeeding structures of societies, like that of individuals, do not substitute one for the other. In the course of the genesis of collective mentalities and individual personalities, they add and superpose themselves just like the *geological strata* of the crust of the earth: the more archaic support the more recent ones and are protected by them from the usual corrosion of time. And this is what constitutes an additional reason to know, if not to rediscover, them.

It is toward the study of these strata, subconscious or unconscious, of individuals in their social groups that we shall henceforth orient ourselves. To this purpose we shall proceed to a psycho-sociological investigation aimed at finding out what health represents nowadays. We shall do it first with individuals responding to an open-ended question, then with those of a study using close-ended questions that respondents did fill in themselves (Parts II and III). We shall also study health by analyzing analogies and symbols with which it is represented (Part IV).

Recapitulation of Part I

1. Health and Salutation

After evoking Greek legend concerning the god-physician Aesclapios and the goddess-health *Hygiè* a rapid comparative **linguistic approach** outlined the encounter of certain terms or expressions tied at the same time to health and to salutation, then their transcriptions into diverse **rites and institutions** of social life. In particular, the Latin etymology makes of health a fundamental value (*valere*), a good without which other goods lose their validity.

Finally, behind legendary and linguistic representations can be discerned the *fundamental attitudes of humans in the face of life and of death*, their behaviors when they are well or ailing. More deeply, health is felt as the most reliable indicator of life and the most tangible guarantee of survival, whether it is envisaged as a reality *before or beyond death*.

Closely linked to the instinct of conservation or of expansion of the self, health sends man back immediately to his daily existence, but, in a more distant fashion, alludes to the *salvation* of religions.

2. Health and Religious Salvation

Just like salutation, **religious salvation** has been expressed by the **Latins** with the same term *salus* as health, as can be verified on the old German *hails*. Such a conjunction in the Latin language led us to a reflection on the historical phenomenon that has constituted, before the advent of **Christianity** and parallel to it, the onslaught of **Oriental salvation religions** into the Roman Empire.

The **Judaic** origins of the Christian conception of salvation has been added to the phenomenon of mystery religions to emphasize the ambivalence of the Latin word *salus*, when it designates at the same time a celestial survival after death and a *terrestrial survival* prior to it. Beyond inevitable divergences, the **parallelism** can be pursued quite naturally between the liturgy of those who are initiated to salvation and the rites of hygiene, between the sacerdotal corps and the medical corps, between sin and illness, between purity and asepsis, etc.

To the point where one may wonder if the ancient idea of *personal salvation* has not, little by little, contributed to the modern socio-juridical notion of *personal health* and if the preoccupation with **eternal health** has not prepared, deep in our personalities, the way to the preoccupation for temporal health of each individual.

At the same time, health has evolved, little by little, toward the status of a *transcultural value* common to all individuals of all cultural areas, and progressively recognized by man.

The institutions of society, specially that of the **language**, have assured the *permanence of deep bonds between health, salutation and religious salvation,* either in the subconscious or unconscious layers of individual personalities, beyond their conscious levels.

PART II

CULTURAL IMAGES
OF HEALTH

Introduction

The most common scientific approaches to health are those of biomedicine, psychology and psychiatry. But the *social* aspect of health is all too often neglected, in spite of the definition presented in the preamble of the World Health Organization to the effect that "Health is a state of complete physical, mental and social well-being, and does not only consist of the absence of disease or infirmity".

Epidemiology, on the other hand, has greatly contributed to highlight sociological and epidemiological parameters.

To summarize the characteristics of the previous approaches, let us state that they are concerned with health behaviors. In other words, in health as it is lived, which one can distinguish from health as it is represented, and which we shall henceforth examine.

To this purpose, let us start again with health behaviors. They are determined or ordered in individuals by the systems or constellations of attitudes shaped through socialization or acculturation in the groups where they belong. (see d'Houtaud 1997a). In the French sociological tradition, that of Durkheim (1972), of Mauss (1923-1925), of Moscovici (1961), of Herzlich (1979), the original concept of behaviors has taken the name of social representations. Opinions and attitudes, in particular derive from the ever-changing universe of representations. In investigations and in surveys it is customary to go back from these last two ones to the first ones.

In other words, representations of health, to which we shall from now on limit ourselves, are expressed in attitudes that translate in health behaviors. Consequently, beyond all investigations bearing on these behaviors, there is room for a psychosocial research entirely oriented toward represented health.

In the next two chapters, we shall summarize, sometimes in transforming them, analyses we developed in three publications: the first two ones (1976 and 1978 a) for chapter 3, the third (1981) for chapter 4. As to chapter 5, it will be based on a communication given at a colloquium in Nancy in 1988 (d'Houtaud A., Field M. G., 1989, b).

Chapter 3

Cultural Images of Health: Findings Based on the Answers of 4,000 Respondents to an Open Ended Question

1. Presentation of the Study and of the Sample

A first inquiry into opinions on health in Lorraine was carried out at the Center of Preventive Medicine of Nancy starting from an open-ended and very broad question: *What is, according to you, the best definition of health?* This question was posed to about one person in 15 among the some 72 000 who presented themselves to a second health examination from January 1971 to May 1974. About one in five failed to answer the question.

We discussed, at length, the **methodology** of this research, the sample, and the results: in the *Revue Internationale d'Education pour la Santé* (d'Houtaud, 1976), in a State *Thesis* ès Lettres et Sciences Humaines (d'Houtaud, 1977), in an article of the *Revue d'Epidémiologie et de Santé Publique* (d'Houtaud, 1978), in an article in *Sociology of Health and Illness* (d'Houtaud, Field, 1984), in two recent books (d'Houtaud A., Field M.G., 1989, a and b), to which we refer the reader for more details.

Let us mention briefly that the **respondents** came from higher socio-economic categories (or S.E.C.), i.e. superior cadres, liberal professions, managers of industry and trade, artisans, to whom we shall refer as "top management" (534), middle management (680), employees (797), workers (997), agricultural workers (125), and those who were not gainfully employed (797 students, housewives and retirees).

These respondents included, according to the regulations then in force, individuals who had been *invited* (drawn by lot from the files of those insured by Social Security) and *volunteers* (among whom were many invited earlier who previously had neglected or refused to respond to the invitation within the time specified): thus, in sum, an average of one acceptance out of three invitations. There is therefore a non-negligible *bias*, which we must consider, particularly in the interpretation of the results. The selection process favored, in each one of the socio-occupational categories, middle class and employees notably, and discriminated against the others, particularly the least well-off from an economic and cultural viewpoint, and those whose working hours were least compatible with the scheduled time of the health examination.

2. The Classification of the 41 Themes by S.E.C. and by Affinities of Meanings

The main results of the inquiry with an open-ended question are shown in Table I, where the five S.E.C., described earlier, are arrayed, at the top, in a descending hierarchical order, and where the 41 definitions of health are grouped into ten themes, on the left-hand side, according to their affinities of meanings and of the S.E.C. where they are predominant.

Thus, at the beginning, each one of the four expressions mentioning *equilibrium* is more frequent among higher and middle classes, as well as their totals at the level of the equilibrium group (23.6% and 19.9% respectively instead of 7.6% among the urban workers, or three times less). And it is the same, for each one of the four definitions associated under the global denomination of the *hedonistic use of life* (respectively 9.4% et 10.4% instead of 3.2% among agricultural workers, or three times less). And for each one of the three definitions of the *reference to the body* (respectively 9.8% and 7.8% instead of 3% among urban workers, or always three times less). The rates of *vitality*, less elevated, oppose above all the middle classes (6%) to agricultural workers (2.4%) and urban workers (2.6%, or two to three times less).

In the **middle** of the distribution of themes, there is the last grouping of four themes, the one of *psychological well-being*, which opposes, in a less contrasted manner, employees (13.7%) and urban workers (13.1%) to the higher classes (8.5%). There remain the two themes of the *value of health* which predominate among rural workers and employees (respectively 10.4% and 9.7% instead of 5.7% among higher classes, or almost two times less). Then the series of nine themes, regrouped under the global rubric of *hygiene*, which predominate among the urban workers and the employees (respectively

15.7% and 13.3% instead of 9.1% among those in agriculture and 9.4% among higher classes, or about half less).

At the end, three groups of themes associate more those in agriculture and urban workers, i.e. manual workers, whether urban or rural. The five themes of *prevention* have higher totals among them (respectively 22% and 20,1% instead of 11.4% among middle classes, or half less). The two themes of physical aptitudes and particularly ability to work (*physical aptitudes*) emerge among rural workers (16.8% instead of 7.8% among the middle classes, or half as often). As to *absence of sickness*, its two themes (particularly that of not to be sick) characterize more the urban workers (16.6% instead of 7.4% among higher classes, or clearly less than half).

Let us specify that all **percentages** are calculated in the vertical columns in relation to the *mentions* of each socio-economic category and, for the column on the right, in relation to the 6 172 mentions. The last line of the table gives the totals of respondents for each column.

3. Opinions, Representations or Social Representation

For greater clarity in our presentation, let us begin with some terminological and conceptual precisions. When we speak of different **opinions on health**, we intend to designate, in a very empirical manner, the diverse responses to the open-ended question, self-filled, when they are associated by S.E.C. or by other groupings (sex, age, educational level, etc) according to their affinities. Their different distributions (d'Houtaud, 1976) correspond to the characteristics of opinions, according to J. Stoetzel and A. Girard (1973), for example in a bell-shape, in U, in L or in J. In associating several groups of definitions or opinions at once in a *thematic* way and, for example, by S.E.C., we are able to extract a plurality of global tendencies which we do not hesitate to call, in the *plural*, **representations or cultural images of health**, according to the strata of the populations where they are most dominant. That plural justifies that *plurality of constellations of opinions on health* by S.E.C. (or by educational level, age, sex, etc). The totality of these constellations or of these differentiated representations also constitutes then what French sociologists have designated, in the singular, by a collective representation or, more often, by a social representation (Durkheim E. 1972; Mauss M. 1923; Moscovici S. 1961; Herzlich C. 1973 and 1979).

Thus, the aim of our investigation is to try to describe and to bring out such pluralities of representations of health in our contemporary society. One should note the difference of approaches and

S.E.C. → THE 41 THEMES OF HEALTH IN 10 GROUPINGS →	higher class	middle class	employees	urban workers	rural workers	not gainfully employed	TOTAL
Life without constraint	5.0	4.6	2.6	2.4	2.0	2.9	3.4
To benefit from life	1.9	3.0	1.6	1.4		2.2	2.0
Not to think of illness	1.6	2.3	0.9	0.6	0.6	1.2	1.3
See the physician as little as possible	0.9	0.5	0.6	0.8	0.6	0.6	0.7
(1) HEDONISTIC USE OF LIFE	9.4	10.4	5.7	5.2	3.2	6.9	7.4
Good physical equilibrium	9.9	7.5	5.5	2.8	3.2	5.1	5.8
Good mental equilibrium	9.0	7.7	5.8	2.6	3.2	5.2	5.8
Good equilibrium	3.4	3.6	3.3	1.6	0.6	3.3	2.9
Equilibrium in the family	1.3	1.1	0.7	0.6	2.7	0.5	0.9
(2) EQUILIBRIUM	23.6	19.9	15.3	7.6	9.7	14.1	15.4
Not to feel one's body	3.5	3.3	1.8	1.5	1.3	4.0	2.7
To feel well 'in one's skin'	4.4	2.9	2.7	0.8	1.9	2.4	2.5
'A healthy mind in a healthy body'	1.9	1.6	0.9	0.7		1.1	1.2
(3) REFERENCE TO THE BODY	9.8	7.8	5.4	3.0	3.2	7.5	6.4
To be able to face all problems	1.6	2.0	1.8	0.9	0.6	1.3	1.5
Optimism	0.7	1.2	1.1	0.5	0.6	0.7	0.8
Not to fear the future	0.6	1.2	0.8	0.5	0.6	0.3	0.7
Personal unfolding	0.9	0.9	0.5	0.2	0.6	0.5	0.6
Dynamism	0.7	0.7	0.2	0.5		0.5	0.5
(4) VITALITY	4.5	6.0	4.4	2.6	2.4	3.3	4.1
Joy of living	3.9	4.8	6.1	5.3	5.3	5.8	5.2
Happiness	2.4	2.7	3.3	2.9	2.6	2.7	2.8
To have a good morale	1.5	1.9	2.7	3.5	1.9	3.4	2.6
To be in good mood	0.7	1.0	1.6	1.4	0.6	1.0	1.2
(5) PSYCHOLOGICAL WELL-BEING	8.5	10.4	13.7	13.1	10.4	12.9	11.8

To have a balanced diet	1.4	1.3	**2.0**	1.7	0.6	*1.7*	*1.6*
To sleep well	0.2	0.7	**0.9**	**0.9**		*0.7*	*0.6*
To live as much as possible in open air	0.4	0.3	**1.0**	**1.1**	0.6	*1.0*	*0.8*
To have a regular life	1.7	2.3	**2.7**	2.4	2.6	*3.4*	*2.5*
To lead a healthy life	2.1	1.7	2.4	**2.8**	1.3	*2.4*	*2.4*
To have a good appetite	0.3	0.8	0.9	**1.4**		*0.8*	*0.8*
To rest	0.5	0.3	0.2	**0.9**		*0.3*	*0.4*
Avoid excesses	1.6	1.5	1.6	**2.3**	**2.7**	*1.1*	*1.8*
Sobriety	0.4	0.4	0.5	**1.0**	**1.3**	*0.3*	*0.5*
Engage in sport	0.8	0.8	1.1	**1.2**		*1.2*	*1.0*
(6) HYGIENE	*9.4*	*10.1*	*13.3*	*15.7*	*9.1*	*12.9*	*12.4*
The essential	2.2	3.5	**5.0**	4.2	**5.9**	*3.0*	*3.7*
The greatest wealth	3.5	3.6	**4.7**	2.0	**4.5**	*3.6*	*3.5*
(7) VALUE OF HEALTH	*5.7*	*7.1*	*9.7*	*6.2*	*10.4*	*6.6*	*7.2*
To have a regular prev. examination	2.8	2.9	3.4	**7.0**	9.7	*4.0*	*4.3*
To watch oneself	3.4	2.9	**5.0**	**5.2**	5.2	*3.9*	*4.2*
To know oneself well	<u>**4.5**</u>	4.0	2.7	**4.9**	5.8	*4.0*	*4.0*
'It is better to prevent than to cure'	1.9	1.5	1.9	**2.3**	1.3	*1.7*	*1.8*
To live as long as possible	0.2	0.1	**0.9**	0.7		*0.1*	*0.4*
(8) PREVENTION	*12.8*	*11.4*	*13.9*	*20.1*	*22.0*	*13.7*	*14.7*
To be at the top of one's form	6.6	5.7	**6.7**	**7.0**	9.7	*5.9*	*6.5*
To be able to work	2.3	2.1	2.0	**2.9**	**7.1**	*2.3*	*2.4*
(9) PHYSICAL APTITUDES	*8.9*	*7.8*	*8.7*	*9.9*	*16.8*	*8.2*	*8.9*
Not to be sick	5.9	6.7	6.6	**10.1**	6.5	*8.4*	*7.6*
To be reg. under med. supervision	**1.5**	2.4	3.4	6.5	5.8	*5.5*	*4.1*
(10) ABSENCE OF SICKNESS	*7.4*	*9.1*	*10.0*	*16.6*	*12.3*	*13.9*	*11.7*
	100.0	*100.0*	*100.0*	*100.0*	*100.0*	*100.0*	*100.0*
Number of mentions	953	1,189	1,279	1,317	154	1,280	6,172
Number of respondents	534	680	797	997	125	867	4,000

Table I: Logical classification of themes of health according to socio-economic category (6,172 mentions from 4,000 individuals who visited the Centre de Médecine Préventive de Nancy from January 1971 to May 1974).

of problematic among Anglo-Saxon authors (Calnan M. 1987 ; Currer C. 1986; Stacey M. 1976 and 1978; Williams R., 1983) and Dutch (Tax B. 1984).

4. The Scalar Structure of the Social Representation of Health

Let us return to Table I, where on each line of the 41 themes we have indicated with heavy characters the predominant percentage(s). We are able to discern an evident **scalar structure** which, roughly, traverses our table along a *diagonal*, going from the left upper corner to the right lower corner.

Let us also immediately observe that 38 of the 41 themes are most prominent in the S.E.C. where the groupings by affinities of meanings predominate. The non-gainfully employed remain apart because of their heterogeneity (students, retirees and housewives who can belong to all S.E.C.). The **three exceptions** are found in the larger groupings of hygiene and of prevention, where the argument of the affinity of meanings was over the socio-occupational aspect. This refers to *avoiding excesses* (2.7% among agricultural workers instead of 2.3% among urban workers): to *sobriety* (1.3% among agricultural workers instead of 1% among urban workers who predominate in the hygiene grouping); to *live as long as possible* (0.9% among employees instead of 0.7% among urban workers, one of the two predominant groupings). The average percentages of these three themes represent respectively 1.8%, 0.4% and 0.4%, or very rigorously 2.6% of the 6,172 mentions. In any case, for the **38 other definitions**, the regrouping of the percentages was done on the basis of the strictly similar *S.E.C. predominance*, where the addition led, quite empirically, to bringing out the scalar structure of representations of health, whose significance we shall from now on examine in greater depth after a new methodological remark.

5. The Empirical Language of the Respondents and the Rational Terminology of the Investigators

It is important, at this stage, to emphasize that, if the 41 fundamental *definitions* are the more or less literal reflection of the empirical language of our **respondents**, on the other hand the denomination of the 10 groupings come from the interpretation and the rational terminology of the language of the **investigators**.

Such a distinction between the more concrete information of the respondents, which is closer to the diversity and the nuances of reality, and their more systematized reformulation by the observer, is based on different processes of apprehending the same reality. In resorting to more abstract schemes of conceptualisation, the interpreter brings *a priori* structures, that generate meanings. One then sees that, if the process of interpretation seems to restrict the *original richness* of the **empirical data**, it brings, on the other hand, the *eventual richness* of **meaning**. The interpretation then appears as a mid-point between the demands of the real in its irreducible *diversity* and those of the rational in its indispensable *simplification*.

Furthermore, **other regroupings** could have been imagined with the same definitions of health. For example, to associate *not to think about illness* (1.3% on the average) with *not to be sick* (7.6%) or to *see the physician as little as possible* (0.7%) with *to be regularly under medical supervision* (4.1%), whereas we have found more significance in dissociating the two preferred understatements of the management (2.5% among top management and 2.8% among middle management instead of 1.2% among agricultural workers) from the two themes of the non-illness (16.6% among urban workers instead of 7.4% among top management) at the two extremities of Table I. Thus, our choice has concretely allowed us to bring out that scalar structure, on which we will comment. At this stage, we suggest that the reader imagine different associations of our numerical data, possibly leading to structures lending themselves to other interpretations.

6. For a Bipolar Interpretation of the Social Representation of Health

Let us go back to our classification of the 41 definitions into 10 synthetic groupings. We propose to characterize the two poles of the latent diagonal of the scalar structure of Table I in the following manner.

The four groupings that predominate among management (*hedonistic use of life, equilibrium, reference to the body, vitality*) manifest, in our opinion, a triple predominance:

– that of the *I*,
– that of a movement of *introversion*,
– that of *personal* norms.

The four groups that predominate on the side of the manual workers (*value of health, prevention, physical aptitudes, absence of sickness*) manifest correlatively three other predominances:

- that of *one* (in French *on*),
- that of *extraversion*,
- that of *social* norms.

Indeed, the higher classes seek in their more *personalized* conception of health a kind of realization of themselves for themselves, to which correspond among manual workers a more *socialized* conception, where the recommended integration of the self tends to be done with society and with the tasks it imposes on individuals. We can see, in these two approaches to health and in these **two types of complementary representations**, a faithful *reflection* of the respective tasks of mastery and of the execution of social tasks.

Let us resort to the opposition of the Latin terms *uti* and *frui* to characterize, on one hand, the tendency toward activities oriented to the useful, toward what is a means to something else, and, on the other, the tendency of activities that are ends in themselves and bring real pleasure. In the first case, health is utilized as a means to arrive at other ends, more for the benefit to society than to the individual. In the second case, it is what gives value to the individual himself, what he seeks for his own benefit Again in the first case it is more or less *expropriated from* the individual. In the second it is *appropriated* by the individual. Between these two polar conceptions of health, individuals and groups oscillate depending on the *interest* they have in society or in the interest they derive from it.

7. From Physical Aptitudes to References to The Body

To better explain the **bi-polar interpretation**, let us go back to the two groupings having to do with *references to the body* (more among management) and to *physical aptitudes* (more among agricultural workers), which lead us to pose the question: **to what ends is the body a privileged point for the useful application of health** (Boltanski L. 1971; Bouet M. 1968)?

In the course of past millenia, the fundamental priority was to *survive*, through physical strength, natural cataclysms, predators, enemies and in hunting game. In our days, physical *work* ensures the continuity of bodily activities in the service of earning one's bread, and thus the survival of families and groups. In that capacity the **body is**

utilized as a work-tool of the individual, laboring inseparably for himself and for society. It is the necessity to be *able to work*, s o important among agricultural workers, (7.1% instead of 2.9% among urban workers and 2% among employees), and that of being *at the top of one's form*, that separates agricultural workers less (9.7%) from the urban workers (7%) and from the middle classes (5.7%). In our automated and robotized society, to be at the top of one's form denotes less and less *aptitudes for work* and more and more *sports performances*. This indirect reference to the body through laborious and sports activities characterizes those in **manual** occupations, particularly those in agriculture.

The reference to the body, in return, is more direct among cadres, whose promotion and *emancipation* in social life involve equally that of their body and, at the same time, its disposability. From that point on, what is to be done of this **body** thus **liberated** from work, if not to locate it at the center of one's personal life, in particular at the center of one's *leisure*? Little by little the body contributes to localize the I in every living organism. Health then appears as the quality making the body apt to promote each individual *ego* toward more and better self-actualization.

8. Vitality and Value of Health

Another way to illustrate the bipolarity of the social representation of health is to observe the socioeconomic variations of the *vitality* grouping (more marked among middle management) and that of the *value of health* (more marked among agricultural workers).

The grouping of the value of health puts together, and apart from the others, **agricultural workers** (10.4%) and the **employees** (9.7%), far from top management (5.7 %) and urban workers (6.2%). The two themes of the *essential* (3.7%) and the *greatest wealth* (3.5%) predominate equally among agricultural workers and among employees (5.9 % and 5% respectively for the first; 4.5% and 4.7%) for the second, the urban workers retaining least the *greatest wealth* (2%) and the higher classes least the *essential* (2.2%). In other terms, the least affluent refer health to **being;** the wealthiest refer health to **wealth.** In the two instances, health appears clearly as the value (the Latin verb *valere* signifies also to be in good health). Without health, other possessions lose their value and with health they acquire more value. Among manual workers, health has an occupational impact such that it is held as the essential and the condition of every other type of wealth.

By contrast, **middle management** have more consideration for the five themes of the *vitality* grouping (6% instead of 2.4% among agricultural workers and 2.6 among urban workers). At that pole, health is not only *personal unfolding, optimism, dynamism,* but *not to be afraid of the future* and to *be able to face all problems of life.* What better way to bring out the **role of health as the purveyor of survival,** assuring a sort of function of *salvation* (the same Latin word *salus* means, at the same time, health and religious salvation)? This grouping is the expression of the individual will to live in the face of the risks and challenges of human existence.

Value and vitality are two complementary formulations in which one can verify the old saying: *Who has health, has everything; who does not, has nothing* (French manuscript of the XVth century).

9. From Prevention to Hygiene, then Equilibrium

The bipolarity seems to recede in the other six other groups of definitions of health: as if it erased itself to leave room to a sort of tertiary **interpretation.** The three groupings of *prevention,* of *hygiene* and of *equilibrium* predominate respectively among *agricultural workers,* among *urban workers,* among *higher management* as three stages: one moves from the countryside to the town; one moves from manual tasks to be executed, to the responsibilities of mastery. These three formulations are models to pose the problem of **semantic contents:** would they be different ways of saying the same thing? As if these three significations, in referring people to the same meaning, fulfilled, in different social strata, equivalent functions. Even in this case, it would not be less *meaningful that health be perceived and represented as equilibrium in proportion to the degree of integration of individuals* in the economic and cultural life of a country.

Preferred by the most deprived strata of modern society, **equilibrium** refers either to an *internal harmony* of individuals (physical or psychological, for example), either to an *external harmony* (with the cosmos or with society). By comparison, **hygiene** figures as an *indispensable counter to the sanitary risks* of large population agglomerations where the propagation and the contagion of infectious diseases are that much more difficult to control, and they assume individuals who are persuaded of its value. As to attitudes of **prevention,** they are naturally prevalent among agricultural workers and those who raise cattle, for whom the most important thing is the *temporal dimension* (the time that flies) of tasks to program from day to day according to the cycles of the seasons, and for whom it is vitally important to face *meteorologically unpredictable situations (the actual weather).*

10. From Non-Sickness to Psychological Well-Being, then to the Hedonistic Use of Life

If we had to find a *tertiary structure* common to the last three groups of definitions of life, it could be to consider them as complementary responses to the question : how to recognize health? One would then pass from an objective negative criterion, *non-illness*, dear to the urban workers (16.6%), to two subjective positive criteria : *psychological well-being* common to urban workers (13.1%) and to employees (13.7%), the *hedonistic use of life*, bringing together the middle management (10.4%) and top management (9.4%).

In non-sickness one can verify the difficulty there is nowadays to perceive and to positively define what is health: one resorts to *sickness*, the opposite of health, and to the *social control* of sickness through medical activities.

Psychological well-being already calls for more personalized responses where, the psyche being the only one to escape social dispossession, health is then evoked with sentiments characteristic of happy moments: *joy of living, happiness, good morale, good humor.*

In rising to the more advantaged strata of society, one activates, in the hedonistic use of life, egocentric attitudes of a more radical *appropriation* of health. Sickness appears decidedly as the radical constraint and health (cf. the Greek goddess *Hygie*) assumes the smiling face of *liberty*, as if it constituted an integral part of the individual personality or of the *ego*.

11. Limits of the Research

Although superior to the *qualitative* methods classic in literature which, earlier, still depended on the intuitive perceptions of the observer, contents analysis of the responses to our open-ended question, even if it tends to satisfy the scientific criteria of *objectivity*, of *faithfulness*, of *validity* and of *generalization*, is not completely devoid of a certain subjectivity: this is why we decided to pursue our research on the representations of health by means of the more *quantitative* and more *standardized* procedures of close-ended questions (cf. the following chapter).

After recalling the limits of a satisfactory quantification in contents analysis, let us recall the difficult problem of terms and their meanings. Do several terms receive in *several* strata the *same* acceptation? And, inversely, does a *single* term receive, in these strata, several acceptations? The way we carried out our inquiry leads us to pose these two questions, not to answer them: for this only a new investigation would do.

12. Orientation of this Research

A first result of this research has already been noted: it was pursued in a **new** investigation and **extended in close-ended questions** in 1978 with a large sample of 11,000 respondents (cf. next chapter), which has permitted the control of the different parameters of age and S.E.C., and to add those of sex, of educational level, and the state of health (d'Houtaud, Field 1986 and 1989 a, chs. 6 to 8).

When we examine the research with an open-ended question, one perceives themes common to *manual* workers and to the *elderly*; others are common to *higher management* and to the *youths*; some, rarer, associate nevertheless *manual workers* and the *youths*, higher management and the elderly. The comparison of **synchronic perspectives** (S.E.C.) and **diachronic** ones (age) brings us to pose the problem of the evolution of individuals in the course of their life trajectory or of that of contemporary *society* where the mentality of the elderly (and of manual worker) would progressively cede its place to those of the younger (and of higher management).

Globally research with an open-ended question on a very large scale has permitted us to perceive the radical *independence* of the **social representation of health** in relation to **that of sickness**, which was present in only 8.9% of the mentions, the social control by physicians having been mentioned only in 4.1% of the mentions, or a total of 11.7% of spontaneous evocations in the responses (a little bit more than 1 in 7).

The **internal contents of the social representation of cultural images of health** reveals itself as being quite varied, going from *physical aptitudes* of health to the *value of health*, from *prevention and hygiene* to *psychological well-being*, then to a *reference to the body*, to *the hedonistic use of life* and to the pluralist notion *of equilibrium*. Or a prodigious efflorescence of 37 positive definitions of health with extraordinarily rich connotations.

Finally, a **socio-occupational structure of the images of health** manifested itself very clearly: *negative* and *socio-centric* themes were mentioned more by manual workers (and the oldest ones), the *positive* and *egocentric* themes being mentioned more often by higher management (and the youngest ones). The diagonal of Table I, ordering definitions of health according to a sort of scale of attitudes, poses the question whether, behind the notion of the S.E.C., the variations are due rather to *economic* connotations (income levels) or to their *cultural* connotations (educational levels). At least our rather informal attempt to reconnoiter the terrain has allowed us to join together *complementary social roles*: those of *execution* *by* *manual* *workers* and those of the *mastery of higher* management in the accomplishment of the required tasks for the functioning of our contemporary society.

Chapter 4

What Does Health Represent: 11,000 Respondents from Lorraine Respond to Five Close-Ended Questions on Health (Nancy, 1978)

1. Presentation of the Investigation and of the Sample

After publication of the results of the **first investigation** using an open-ended question administered to 4 000 respondents from 1971 to 1974 (see previous chapter), **a second investigation** was carried out in 1978 with 11 000 respondents using *close-ended* questions, as part of the regular questionnaires administered during a preventive health examination at the Center of Preventive Medicine in Vandoeuvre-lès-Nancy.

The results of this research have been published and discussed in the *Revue internationale d'éducation pour la Santé* (d'Houtaud, 1981), in the book *Concepts of Health, Illness and Disease: A Comparative Perspective* of C. Currer and M. Stacey (d'Houtaud, Field, 1986), in two recent works (d'Houtaud, Field, 1989 a and b) to which we refer the reader for more details.

The **sample**, representing the totality of those who came to the Center of Preventive Medicine during 7 to 8 months of 1978, consists of:

- by sex, of 5,247 men and 5,724 women
- by age, of 3,008 adults from 18 to 29 years of age, of 3,194 from 30 to 39, of 2,587 from 40 to 49, of 1,719 from 50 to 59 and of 493 aged 60 and over

- by *socio-economic categories or classes:*
  - 109 artisans and owners or managers of industry and trade,
  - 906 higher managers and members of liberal professions,
  - 1,902 middle managers,
  - 1,471 employees,
  - 1,617 qualified workers and foremen,
  - 921 specialized workers and laborers,
  - 548 service personnel,
  - 137 members of the armed forces, police and others,
  - 1,814 not gainfully employed persons (students, housewives, retirees),
  - 1,259 who did not want to identify themselves, or did not know, their socio-economic category as listed above.

2. Retained Questions

In a questionnaire usually used for a preventive health examination, it was obviously impossible to use the 41 definitions of health obtained by the open-ended question: in fact space was available for only 4 questions with 4 to 5 items each.

We decided to take up literally **10 definitions of health**, selected because of the high proportion given by the respondents or of their thematic importance and regrouped in Table II in the two questions under C (*not to feel one's body, not to be sick, to know oneself well, to be able to face all problems of life, to feel well in one's skin*) and E (*personal unfolding, to have a good morale, joy of living, equilibrium, to be at the top of one's form*). Here the formulations come from the **respondents** themselves to the open-ended question.

The **other 8 definitions**, regrouped into 2 questions (B and D) of Table II, come from the **investigators**: they have synthesized into 8 great themes the 31 definitions of health not taken up under C and E: *hygiene, work, medicine, leisure* under D: *to have luck, physical resistance, precautions, to have good conditions of life and of work* under B.

ANSWERS → QUESTIONS ↓	YES %	NO %	NA %	CHOICES %
Questions A: Which one of these two formulations, everything considered, do you prefer?				
1. If one is sick, it is *because it must be*				*18.5*
2. One can always *avoid* a sickness				*73.8*
No answers (choices)				*7.3*
Questions B: To be in good health is:				
1. To have luck	**41.5**	44.3	14.2	*8.6*
2. To have physical resistance	**70.2**	18.7	11.1	*21.1*
3. To take precautions	**75.1**	14.5	10.4	*19.6*
4. To have good conditions of life and work	**83.5**	8.9	7.6	*42.9*
No answers (choices)				*7.8*
Questions C: To be healthy is:				
1. Not to feel one's body	**37.2**	43.4	19.4	*3.0*
2. Not to be sick	**70.9**	16.3	12.8	*25.4*
3. To know oneself well	**60.8**	23.3	15.9	*9.7*
4. To be able to face all problems of life	**63.1**	22.3	14.6	*13.7*
5. To feel well in one's skin	**83.3**	8.3	8.4	*41.6*
No answers (choices)				*6.6*
Questions D: To remain in good health comes from:				
1. Hygiene	**90.5**	4.2	5.3	*54.3*
2. Work	**57.2**	28.1	14.7	*9.7*
3. Medicine	**71.8**	15.7	12.5	*19.9*
4. Leisure	**61.8**	23.0	15.2	*7.0*
No answers (choices)				*9.1*
Questions E: What corresponds best to the definition of health?				
1. Personal unfolding	**56.3**	25.5	18.2	*5.1*
2. Good morale	**73.3**	13.7	13.0	*19.5*
3. Joy of living	**68.1**	16.7	15.2	*14.6*
4. Equilibrium	**78.6**	10.3	11.1	*30.7*
5. To be at the top of one's form	**75.8**	11.5	12.7	*25.4*
No answers (choices)				*4.7*

Table II. List of questions on health and global percentages of answers by YES or NO and by CHOICES on the part of 11,002 respondents at the Center of Preventive Medicine (Nancy), 1978.

Thus there are 18 items, to which respondents answered individually by YES or NO (or No Answer), and at the level of each one of the four questions, by CHOICE of the most important element in the opinion of each respondent.

The same observations can be made concerning the representativeness of this sample as was done for the previous investigation by the open-ended question.

To the 18 items are added the **two propositions** (fatalistic or non-fatalistic) of question A, taken from an earlier investigation at the Center of Preventive Medicine (1975).

Let us remark that the modality of response by YES or NO allows comparisons among the 18 items of questions B, C, D, E, whereas the modality of response by CHOICE (more constraining, more directive) allows comparisons only within each one of the 5 questions, in which the score of each item depends probably on the environment of the other themes.

3. Responses by YES or NO and by CHOICE to the Five Close-Ended Questions

Table II provides **a general presentation of the results** from the 11 000 respondents, without distinction of sex, age or S.E.C. It gives us a first approximation of the respective importance of the 20 retained themes.

a) On the YES side, only one definition goes over the 90 % mark:
 – *hygiene* (90.5 %)
Followed at more than 80 % by:
 – *good conditions of life and of work* (83.5 %),
 – *to feel well in one's skin* (83.3 %).
Around 75 % one encounters:
 – *equilibrium* (78.6 %),
 – *at the top of one's form* (75.8 %),
 – *precautions* (75.1 %),
 – *good morale* (73.3 %).
Near the 70 % there are:
 – *medicine* (71.8 %),
 – *not to be sick* (70.9 %),
 – *physical resistance* (70.2 %),
 – *joy of living* (68.1 %).
In the proximity of 60 % one finds:
 – *to be able to face all problems of life* (63.1 %),
 – *leisure* (61.8 %),

– to know oneself well (60.8 %),
– work (57.2 %),
– personal unfolding (56.3 %).
Only two definitions do not reach the 50% mark:
– to have luck (41.5 %),
– not to feel one's body (37.2 %).

b) On the side of CHOICES, let us set aside the question about fatalism, to which less than one respondent in five suscribed.

Five definitions hold the first places in the same order:
– hygiene (54.3 %),
– good conditions of life and of work (42.9 %),
– to feel well in one's skin (41.6 %),
– equilibrium (30.7 %),
– to be at the top of one's form (25.4 %).
That one is rejoined by:
– not to be sick (25.4 %).
Then,
– physical resistance (21.1 %),
– medicine (19.9 %),
come before the first two of the following four:
– precautions (19.6 %),
– good morale ((19.5 %),
– joy of living (14.6%),
– to the able to face all problems of life (13.7 %).
Among the last six ones:
– to know oneself well (9.7 %),
– work (9.7 %),
– to have luck (8.6 %),
which come before:
– leisure (7 %),
which are followed at the end of the list by:
– personal unfolding (5.1 %),
– not to feel one's body (3 %).

These two lists show **two almost identical hierarchizations**, except for some permutations. They give the reader an idea of the *impact* of the 18 themes on 11,000 Lorrains undergoing a preventive health examination.

Let us also note the **parallelism of the no-answers with the NOs** whose fluctuations they attenuate: those who *hesitate* to answer appearing as the diminishing shadow of those who *oppose*.

4. The Comparison of the Global Results of the Two Investigations

At this general stage of the results with *close-ended questions*, it is important to undertake a **comparison** with those responses to an **open-ended question**.

a) The ten common items are reproduced in Table III.

If one compares the 10 items in the two investigations,
- *to be at the top of one's form* keeps its percentage (13.3 % and 13.5 %),
- *not to be sick* decreases slightly from the open-ended question (15.7 %) to the close-ended question (13.4 %).

What is Health	Answers			
	open-ended questions N=4,000		close-ended questions N=11,002	
	N	%	N	%
1. To feel well in one's skin	156	5.2	4.580	22.1
2. Equilibrium	950	31.6	3.378	16.3
3. To be at the top of one's form	401	13.3	2.798	13.5
4. Not to be sick	472	15.7	2.789	13.4
5. Good morale	162	5.4	2.141	10.3
6. Joy of living	324	10.8	1.612	7.8
7. To be able to face all problems	92	3.0	1.507	7.2
8. To know oneself well	248	8.2	1.062	5.1
9. Personal unfolding	37	1.2	557	2.7
10. Not to feel one's body	169	5.6	329	1.6
Totals of the 10 terms	3,011	100.0	20.753	100.0

Table III: The frequency of the ten themes common to the two investigations by an open-ended question and close-ended questions.

The themes that decreased are:
- *equilibrium* (from 31.6 % to 16.3 %, or fifty percent less),
- *not to feel one's body* (from 5.6 % to 1.6 %, or 4 times less),
- *joy of living* (from 10.8 % to 7.8 %, or almost one third less),
- *to know oneself well* (from 8.2 % to 5.1 %).

The themes on the increase are:
- *to feel well in one 's skin* (from 5.2 % to 22.1 %, or 4 times more),
- *good morale* (from 5.4 % to 10.3 %, or twice),
- *to be able to face all problems of life* (from 3 % to 7.2 % or double),
- *personal unfolding* (from 1.2 % to 2.7 %).

This comparison was done on the basis of *recalculated percentages* at the level of the 10 common themes, proportionately to the number of responses by CHOICE. Nevertheless, it offers an order of size, where a quite close **hierarchization of themes** subsists, the permutations affecting most often two neighboring items. These modifications can easily be explained because of the differentiated approaches of the two investigations: the *open question* called for the analogies and the symbols that emerged in the imagination of the **respondents**, whereas in the close-ended questions the formulations were selected by the **investigators**.

b) Among the eight other themes of the second investigation, four received less distant formulations in the open-ended question and in the close-ended questions. The most stable concerns the physician or *medicine* (19 % and 19.2 % respectively). *Work* goes down slightly (from 11.4 % to 9.4 %). The decrease of *precautions is from the double to the single (from 39.4 % to 19 %)*, whereas *hygiene* increases not far from the single to the double (from 30.2 % to 52.4 %).

5. Analysis of Correspondences Through Correlating Sociological Variables With the YES or NO Responses, With Double Exposure of Responses By CHOICE

A synthetic overview of the results with 11,000 respondents to the close-ended questions is given in Figure 1, in an **analysis of correspondences** obtained by correlating *sociological variables* with the *YES and NO* responses and the responses *by* CHOICE being presented in double exposure.

It is a question of a simplification realized in such a way that the **YES and NO answer** are transcribed at the *four corners* of the figure; the **sociological parameters** are located near the *origin of the axes;* **answers by CHOICES** are in an intermediate position.

a) globally one observes that axis 1 separates:
   - all the *YES* which are concentrated in the two lower quadrants
   - all the *NO* which are concentrated in the two higher quadrants

b) The CHOICES of the 20 items spread out unequally:
   - 5 in the *higher left* quadrant,
   - 3 in the *higher right* quadrant,
   - 6 in the *lower left* quadrant,
   - 6 in the *lower right* quadrant.

c) The **age** follows a vaguely *parabolic* form, those less than 30 years old being localized in the higher left quadrant and those over 60 on the higher right quadrant.

d) The S.E.C are spread out approximately along a **diagonal**, where the top management (the **cadres**) are in the lower left quadrant and manual workers in the higher right quadrant.

e) **The most positive themes** in responses by YES or NO are distributed along the *diagonal of the S.E.C*, the top management endorsing them, the manual workers rejecting them.

f) **The most negative themes** are distributed along the *diagonal perpendicular* to the previous one, the YESses coming from the not gainfully employed persons and the 40-59 years old adults, and the NOs from the younger ones.

g) The CHOICES of the two *left quadrants* (the younger ones and top management) refer to the rather **positive** definitions of health; those of the two *right quadrants* (the oldest and manual workers) refer to the rather **negative** definitions of health. However certain themes are located at the border of the two quadrants: *hygiene* between top management and the young ones; *precautions* and *to know oneself well* between the young and the manual workers.

h) Needless to say, in conclusion, how much this analysis of correspondences *faithfully reflects the previous descriptions* concerning the totality of 11 000 respondents. Before pursuing analyses, at the level of the S.E.Cs and age groups, we shall study the influence of fatalistic and non-fatalistic attitudes (question A of Table II) on the 18 themes (questions B, C, D and E of Table II).

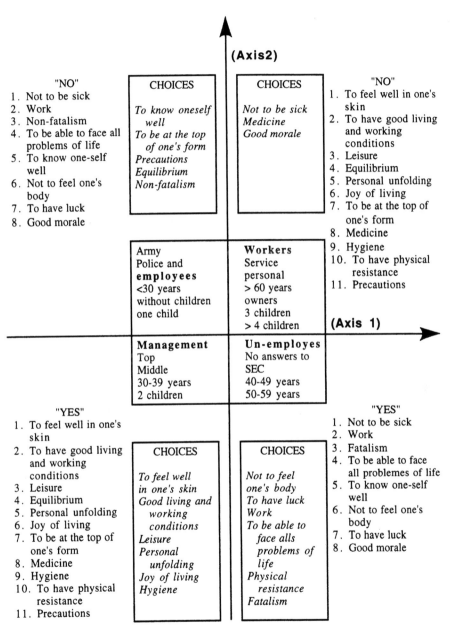

Figure I : Schema of themes on health : answers by **yes** or by **no** and by **choices,** according to some sociological variables.

6. The Influence of the Fatalistic and Non-Fatalistic Tendencies on the Choice of the 18 Items

Almost three-fourths of the respondents have, according to Table IV, adopted a non-fatalistic attitude in the face of illness and less than 1 in 5 a fatalistic attitude.

QUESTIONS	ANSWERS
	Choices %
Question V: Which of the following formulations, all things considered, do you prefer?	
1. If one is sick, it is because one must be	18.9
2. One can always avoid a sickness	73.8
No answers	7.3
Total	100.0

Table IV: The *fatalistic* and *non-fatalistic* tendency in matters of health.

This question was posed only to manifest the eventual incidence of these two contrary attitudes on the responses to the 18 themes.

In Table V the percentages are, for practical reasons, on the horizontal lines: one asks oneself how many have opted for each one of these two attitudes among those who have retained the 18 themes.

On the side of the **fatalistic attitude** (18.9 %). one observes in decreasing order:

 – *to have luck* (42.6 %).
 – *not to feel one's body* (29.6 %).
 – *physical resistance* (27.3 %).
 – *work* (26.1 %).
 – *not to be sick* (24 %).
 – *good morale* (23.8 %).

On the side of the **non-fatalistic attitude** (73.8 %). one observes similarly:

 – *precautions* (89%).
 – *to know oneself well* (87.6 %).

– *good conditions of living and work* (83.4 %).
– *equilibrium* (82.6 %).
– *to feel well in one's skin* (81.2%).

One remarks that *good fortune* manifests itself more strongly on the side of *fatalism*, as well as *precautions* and *to know oneself well* in the side of non-fatalism.

DEFINITIONS OF HEALTH	ANSWERS		
	Fatalistic attitude	Non-fatalistic attitude	Total %
A. Health comes from:			
1. Hygiene	19.6	80.4	100.0
2. Good living and working conditions	16.6	83.4	100.0
3. Physical resistance	27.3	72.7	100.0
4. Medicine	19.3	80.7	100.0
5. Precautions	11.0	89.0	100.0
6. Work	26.1	73.9	100.0
7. To have luck	42.6	57.4	100.0
8. Leisure	19.0	81.0	100.0
B. Health is:			
1. To feel well in one's skin	18.8	81.2	100.0
2. Equilibrium	17.4	82.6	100.0
3. To be at the top of one's form	20.8	79.2	100.0
4. Not to be sick	24.0	76.0	100.0
5. Good morale	23.8	76.2	100.0
6. Joy of living	20.2	79.8	100.0
7. To be able to face all problem of life	20.6	79.4	100.0
8. To know oneself well	12.4	87.6	100.0
9. Personal unfolding	21.2	78.8	100.0
10. Not to feel one's body	29.6	70.4	100.0

Table V: *Fatalistic* and *non-fatalistic* tendencies in the two series of themes on health.

7. The Predominance of Definitions of Health According to Age

According to Table VI six themes (*to have good conditions for living and work, leisure, to feel well in one's skin, joy of living, equilibrium* and *personal unfolding*) predominate among those who are **under 40** and two others (*hygiene* and *to be at the top of one's form*) among those under 50: those are the most *positive* and the most *egocentric* definitions, that characterize more the **youngest**.

Two themes (*to have luck, not to feel one's body*) emerge clearly among those **60 and over**. Four others (*not to be sick, medicine, work, good morale*) among those **50 and over**. Three others (*physical resistance, precautions, to know oneself well*) among those **40 and over**. The last one characterizes the **40 to 59 years old** (*to be able to face all problems of life*). One recognizes that the most *negative* and the most *sociocentric* definitions of health are found more often among the elderly.

THEMES	AGE GROUPS				
	18 - 29 years	30 - 39 years	40 - 49 years	50 - 59 years	60 years and over
1. To have good living and working conditions	51.7	52.0	41.6	38.5	31.4
2. Leisure	10.8	8.2	6.3	4.1	4.4
3. To feel well in one's skin	49.8	49.9	40.2	35.1	33.8
4. Joy of living	17.8	16.3	13.7	13.4	9.5
5. Equilibrium	33.4	34.7	31.3	28.0	27.5
9. Hygiene	60.5	60.3	60.2	57.3	57.3
11. Personal unfolding	5.8	6.0	4.9	4.5	2.9
13. To be at the top of one's form	27.8	26.9	26.8	24.9	24.4
6. To know oneself well	8.5	9.8	11.1	12.7	13.7
7. Take precautions	20.4	19.8	22.0	22.6	28.6
8. To be able to face all problems of life	11.6	13.3	17.6	18.1	15.8
10. Good morale	15.3	16.2	23.3	29.1	35.7
12. Work	7.5	9.8	12.2	14.7	14.9
14. To have physical resistance	20.9	19.7	25.1	27.9	26.5
15. Medicine	21.3	21.8	21.2	23.9	23.4
16. To have luck	6.9	8.5	11.3	10.9	13.5
17. Not to feel one's body	3.2	3.3	2.9	3.1	5.0
18. Not to be sick	27.0	23.8	28.3	30.9	31.8
19. Fatalism	19.3	21.3	19.8	21.5	20.6

Table VI: Variations of choices of the 18 items on health and fatalism by age groups.

THEMES	S.E.C					
	High management	Middle management	Employ-ees	Qualified workers Foremen	Specialized workers Ordinary workers	Service personnel
1. To have good living and working conditions	52.7	53.6	50.6	49.0	40.8	40.8
2. Leisure	9.3	10.0	6.8	8.6	6.9	5.7
3. To feel well in one's skin	52.9	52.6	47.2	37.6	33.8	42.9
5. Equilibrium	44.2	39.1	35.1	27.2	21.3	30.3
9. Hygiene	64.3	60.3	60.1	57.1	52.9	61.8
11. Personal unfolding	7.2	6.7	4.4	3.5	3.7	3.6
17. Not to feel one's body	5.9	3.1	3.0	3.1	3.3	1.4
4. Joy of living	14.0	16.6	15.4	18.4	13.7	13.7
6. To know oneself well	10.3	12.3	9.0	9.9	11.2	8.6
8. To be able to face all problems of life	13.6	12.5	13.8	16.6	13.8	18.4
15. Medicine	18.5	19.1	24.3	21.1	23.5	21.6
7. Take preecautions	16.4	17.9	17.0	22.3	24.8	24.2
10. Good morale	7.5	10.7	18.9	24.2	28.4	27.9
12. Work	7.8	10.6	8.8	13.2	16.6	10.9
13. To be at the top of one's form	27.1	26.9	26.2	26.7	32.9	24.5
14. To have physical resistance	22.8	21.2	24.5	20.1	21.7	25.4
16. To be fortunate	8.1	7.3	7.9	8.6	12.7	9.6
18. Not to be sick	17.3	19.5	27.0	32.8	38.0	28.8
19. Fatalism	20.6	18.5	20.9	19.9	22.5	24.0

Table VII: Choices of the 18 themes on health and on fatalistic attitude by the six socio-economic categories.

8. The Predominance of Definitions of Health According to S.E.C.

Table VII takes up again *the 18 definitions of health.* but in substituting S.E.C for age groups in the preceeding table. Because of the large sample size (11,000) it was felt important to distinguish qualified workers, specialized workers and service personnel. One should note in 1978 the *absence of agricultural workers*, the Mutualité Agricole (agricultural insurance group) refusing to assume any longer the financial responsibility for a preventive health examination at the Center for Preventive Medicine, which, from the strict viewpoint of research, is also deplorable.

The heavy characters make it easier to perceive the **scalar structure** of this table, as in the preceding one. One should note that among the 7 themes that predominate among top management, 6 were already predominant among the young (*not to feel one's body* puts top management closest to the oldest). Similarly, among the 7 last themes that predominate among the **specialized workers** and service personnel, 6 were already predominant among the oldest (*to be at the top of one's form* being common to **top management** and **employees**, as well as to the oldest).

9. The Synchronic and Diachronic Dimensions in The Open-Ended Question and in Close-Ended Questions

Among the ten themes common to the two studies, the following can be observed.

a) Concerning age:

- 5 definitions of health dominate among the **younger** ones:
    - *to feel well in one's skin*
    - *equilibrium,*
    - *to be at the top of one's form,*
    - *joy of living,*
    - *personal unfolding;*

- 3 dominate among the **older ones:**
    - *good morale,*
    - *to know oneself well,*
    - *to be able to face all problems of life*

- 2 move from the **youngest to the oldest**:
  . *not to be sick,*
  . *not to feel one's body.*

b) Concerning the S.E.C.:

- 4 definitions of health dominate among **management:**
  - *to feel well in one 's skin,*
  - *equilibrium,*
  - *personal unfolding,*
  - *not to feel one's body.*

- 4 *remain among* **manual** *workers:*
  - *good morale,*
  - *not to be sick,*
  - *to be at the top of one's form,*
  - *joy of living.*

- 2 change:
  - *to know oneself well* moves from manual workers to middle management and to specialized workers,
  - *to be able to face all problems of life* moves from management to **qualified workers.**

c) In combining age and S.E.C.

- 3 remain common to **management** and to the **youngest:**
  - *to feel well in one's skin,*
  - *equilibrium,*
  - *personal unfolding;*

- 1 remains common to **manual worker** and to the **oldest:**
  - *good morale*

- 2 remain common to **manual workers** and to the **youngest:**
  - *-to be at he top of one's form,*
  - *joy of living;*

- 3 change:
  - *to know oneself well* passes from **manual workers** and the **oldest** to **management** and the **oldest:**
  - *not to feel one's body* passes from **management** and the **youngest** to **management** and the **oldest**
  - *not to be sick* passes from the **manual workers** and the **youngest** to the **manual workers** and **the oldest**.

- 1 fluctuates in a less clear manner:
  - *to be able to face all problems of life* passes from **management, employees** and **the oldest** to **manual workers** and **the oldest**.

In the last four changes, only one parameter is modified, i.e. either age, or the S.E.C. The *scalar structure acquired from the close-ended questions* seems the most *satisfying*. In sum, the **scalar structure** is confirmed in the two studies. The major positive definitions remain common to management and the youngest, but one single negative definition remains common to manual workers and to the oldest.

However, these solidarities between S.E.C. and age can be questioned in view of the fact that the two *parameters remain dependent:* there are more manual workers among the older respondents and more aged ones among the workers; the educational levels of the youngest orient them more rapidly toward managerial roles.

Hence, our decision to deal now with socio-economic variations within age groups and with age groups within S.E.C s.

10. The Variations of the Definitions of Health According to the Parameters of Age and S.E.C. Independently One from the Other

We carried out this study in a systematic fashion in another work (d'Houtaud, Field, 1989 a, Ch 7). Here we shall limit ourselves to some examples to demonstrate that the **variations by S.E.C.** exist independently of *those of age* and the **variations by age** independently of *those by S.E.C.s.*

Inasmuch as those who have retired do not have the opportunity to mention their previous occupation and that heads of households aged 65 and over are not invited to go through a preventive health examination, we have constituted four 10 year *age groups* under that **age** limit (20-29, 30-39, 40-49, 50-59). As to S.E.C.s we have kept only the *three levels* numerically best represented in the two sexes: management, employees, workers, adding on the female side the important category of women who are not gainfully employed.

Let us also point out that the percentages in the two following tables do not add up either horizontally or vertically because they themselves are extracted from the more complex tables we drew out: here they can be read in the two directions of the tables. Although our sample is rather large (11,000), it happens that some cells have small numbers and that there are random variations: this is why we shall avoid, in the examples cited, definitions of health that were little mentioned in the CHOICES of the respondents.

A. To Feel Well in One's Skin

Among men (M) as among women (F), the expression *to feel well in one's skin* (Table VIII) is the object of more responses by CHOICES among:

- **management** than among workers in all age groups of the two sexes,
- **those less than 40** than their elders (with the sole exception of male employees of 40-49) in all S.E.C.s and the two sexes.

It culminates among male management 30-39 (56 %) and female (61.5 %). It is less often mentioned by female workers 50-59 (26.8 %), by male employees 50-59 (26 %), male workers 40-49 (29. 5 %), by workers 50-59, men (27.8 %) and women (26.8 %).

S.E.C	S.E.C.	AGE			
		20 to 29	30 to 39	40 to 49	50 to 59
M	a) management b) employees c) workers	**51.7** **52.8** **42.0**	**56.0** 40.3 40.2	45.4 47.8 29.5	38.4 26.0 27.8
F	a) management b) employees c) workers	**56.9** **50.5** **47.1**	**61.5** **51.1** **47.6**	55.4 43.2 35.0	39.3 42.9 26.8
	d) unemployed	**55.8**	50.0	40.0	45.0

Table VIII: To feel well in ones skin as a definition of health: percentages compared by S.E.C. and by sex (M and F) in four age groups.

In spite of some rare and weak irregularities, when one combines the effects of age and S.E.C, the sentiment of *feeling well in one's skin* increases quite strongly when one goes up **social strata** in each one of the 4 age groups and it decreases when one goes up the **age groups** in each one of the 7 S.E.C.s.

In the example (not cited here in the table) of *equilibrium*, the regular increases are verified in going up social strata in each age group, but not in going up the group in each S.E.C.

The case of being *at the top of one's form* is even more picturesque: no systematic increase either by age or by S.E.C.

B. Good Morale

Good morale varies in Table IX exactly inversely *to feel well in one's skin* in the previous one. In other words, the proportions increase

- **from management to workers** in all age groups of two sexes (the women who are not gainfully employed being put aside),
- **from those less than 30 years to those 50-59** in all S.E.C.s and the two sexes.

The extreme fluctuations go from 6.4 % among female managers 20-29 to 45.5 % among female workers 50-59, or 7 times more.

The case of *not being sick* is the inverse of that of *equilibrium*: decrease of percentages in going up **social strata** in most age groups of the two sexes (the Women who are not gainfully employed being put aside); a kind of stability in going up **age** in almost all the S.E.C.s of the two sexes.

SEX	S.E.C.	AGE			
		20 to 29	30 to 39	40 to 49	50 to 59
M	a) management b) employees c) workers	7.9 16.7 19.3	8.3 18.1 18.1	12.0 15.2 24.6	14.7 28.0 30.3
F	a) management b) employees c) workers	6.4 18.5 20.8	9.9 15.1 28.4	13.9 22.7 27.2	14.8 22.2 45.5
	d) unemployed	19.5	18.6	25.6	28.2

Table IX: **Good morale:** as a definition of health: compared percentages by S.E.C. and by sex (M and F) in the four age groups.

c- Because of space limitations, we cannot pursue the detailed study of the 18 definitions of health (cf d'Houtaud, Field, 1989 a): that would be the only valid way of approaching their **synchronic and diachronic dimensions;** and to arrive at the demonstration of the fact that certain of them are common to management and the youngest, and others to manual workers and the oldest. The two themes studied above are sufficient, nevertheless, to show that *variations by age exist independently of socio-occupational categories* and vice versa.

11. Orientations and Limits of This Study

The results of the previous investigation by an open-ended question could still raise some questions because of the peculiarities of the method and of the sample.

But, **another methodology,** that of *close-ended questions* self-administered and with a larger sample, has allowed us to find a similar **scalar structure** simultaneously by S.E.C. and by age as in the previous investigation with an open-ended question. The manual exploitation of the first one having been replaced by that of the computer in the second one, it was possible to make the two parameters of age and S.E.C. *independent* of each other, and thus to establish the *permanence of the socio-occupational variations in each age group and age-variations in each S.E.C..* We did not take up studies by certain cultural parameters (educational level, number of books read in the previous year, number of hours of television viewing) and *health* parameters (state of health felt subjectively and measured objectively). For such inquiries we refer the reader to our recent work (d'Houtaud, Field, 1989 a, chs, 6-8).

As to the significance of the variations of definitions of health, we refer the reader to our discussion and comments (d'Houtaud, Gueguen, 1989 b).

However, the irregularities of certain variations of definitions of health in correlating S.E.C.s and age groups have revealed the numerical **limitations** of our sample, and even more in varying the definitions of health by age groups in the S.E.C.s and by the S.E.C in age groups.

Chapter 5

A Comparative Study of the Image of Health in Nancy (France) and in Nijmegen (Netherlands)

In the two previous chapters, we examined the responses of a population at first to an open-ended question and then to four close-ended questions. These two studies were done in Nancy. In order to throw some comparative light on this problem, we want to report on a study that **compared a population in the Netherlands (Nijmegen) with the Nancy sample.**

In Nancy (1978) it will be remembered (Ch. 4) a sample of 11, 000 respondents participated in our research; in Nijmegen (1983), 3,000 persons participated.

We present here five tables: two reflecting the main results of the open-ended question; two other tables comparing the results of the four close-ended questions in Nancy and Nijmegen; and one table to study the distribution of the data as a function of socio-economic category (SEC).

1. Major Results of Answers to the Open-Ended Question

Table X recapitulates the data obtained with 4,000 respondents in Nancy from 1971 to 1974. These are groupings based on the 41 principal themes emerging from a contents analysis of responses to an open-ended question in the rows, the five socio-economic categories being in the columns.

On the one hand, *equilibrium, reference to the body, hedonistic use of life* receive higher proportions of responses from management (top and middle).

On the other hand, *absence of sickness, physical aptitudes, prevention* receive higher proportions of responses from **rural and urban workers** than from the higher classes.

The other four groupings of themes occupy an intermediate position among employees, in association either with management *(vitality)*, or with urban workers *(psychological well-being, hygiene)*, or with rural workers *(value of health)*.

We have used heavy characters to indicate the predominant proportions of each grouping of themes. A **scalar structure** emerges: Table XI provides the essential dimensions of that structure.

The 41 Themes of Health	S.E.C.						TOTAL
	higher class	middle class	em-ployees	urban workers	rural worker	not gainfully em-ployed	
(1) Equilibrium	**23.6**	19.9	15.3	7.6	9.7	14.1	15.4
(2) Reference to the body	**9.8**	7.8	5.4	3.0	3.2	7.5	6.4
(3) Hedonistic use of life	9.4	**10.4**	5.7	5.2	3.2	6.9	7.4
(4) Vitality	4.5	**6.0**	4.4	2.6	2.4	3.3	4.1
(5) Psychological well-being	8.5	10.4	**13.7**	13.1	10.4	12.9	11.8
(6) Hygiene	9.4	10.1	13.3	**15.7**	9.1	12.9	12.3
(7) Absence of sickness	7.4	9.1	10.0	**16.6**	12.3	13.9	11.7
(8) Value of health	5.7	7.1	9.7	6.2	**10.4**	6.6	7.2
(9) Prevention	12.8	11.4	13.9	20.1	**22.0**	13.7	14.7
(10) Physical aptitudes	8.9	7.8	8.7	9.9	**16.8**	8.2	8.9
Totals	100.0	100.0	100.0	100.0	100.0	100.0	100.0
Number of mentions	953	1,189	1,279	1,317	154	1,280	6,172
Number of respondents	534	680	797	997	125	867	4,000

Table X: Logical classification of 10 synthetic groups recapitulating 41 principal themes or basic definitions of health according to socio-economic category (6.172 mentions from 4.000 individuals who visited the Centre de Médecine Préventive de Nancy from January 1971 to May 1974).

It can be noted, on the one hand, that *equilibrium, reference to the body,* and the *hedonistic use of life* receive percentages that are 2 to 3 times higher among **management** (or cadres) than among **workers**.

One can thus see that in going down the social class structure, one moves from *the most positive themes*, in which health is the most appropriated by individuals and oriented toward their egocentric advantages, to *themes that are most negative*, where health is the most alienated from individuals and placed more at the service of the sociocentric demands of the collectivity.

Thus the image of health varies along a **scale** that associates simultaneously its conceptual contents and its social dimensions.

			S.E.C.		
Headings **(thematic groups)**	higher class	middle class	employees	urban workers	rural workers
(1) EQUILIBRIUM	++	+	+		
(2) REFERENCE TO THE BODY	++	+			
(3) HEDONISTIC USE OF LIFE	+	++			
(4) VITALITY	+	++	+		
(5) PSYCHOLOGICAL WELL-BEING			++	+	
(6) HYGIENE			+	++	
(7) VALUE OF HEALTH			+		++
(8) ABSENCE OF SICKNESS				++	+
(9) PHYSICAL APTITUDES				+	++
(10) PREVENTION				+	++

Table XI: The 10 groups of the themes of health and the socio-economic zones of their predominance. A cross (+) indicate the S.E.C. where the group has a percentage higher than the average. A double cross (++) indicates the S.E.C. where the percentage is the highest.

2. Major Results of Answers to the Four Close-Ended Questions in Nancy and Nijmegen

The data in Table XII can be distinguished from the two previous ones on two points:

- there are four close-ended questions whose multiple items were proposed to respondents in two forms: YES or NO to

each one of the items; then, among the items of each question, a CHOICE of the one that appeared the most important to them (this was the only modality retained in this table)
- it is a comparison between the viewpoints of the 3,000 respondents of the health region of Nijmegen in 1983 with that of the 11,000 persons who underwent a health check-up in the region of Nancy in 1978.

RESPONSES BY CHOICES → QUESTIONS ↓	NANCY %	NIJMEGEN %
Question I: To be in good health is:		
1. To have luck	8.6	7.4
2. To have physical resistance	21.1	24.1
3. To take precautions	19.6	5.4
4. To have good living and working conditions	42.9	62.0
No answers	7.8	1.1
Question II: To be healthy is:		
1. Not to feel one's body	3.0	3.7
2. Not to be sick	25.4	18.4
3. To know oneself well	9.7	8.3
4. To be able to face all problems	13.7	21.9
5. To feel well in one's skin	41.6	47.2
No answers	6.6	0.5
Question III: To remain in good health comes from:		
1. Hygiene	54.3	68.4
2. Work	9.7	7.7
3. Medicine	19.9	12.5
4. Leisure	7.0	9.0
No answers	9.1	2.4
Question IV: Which is the best definition of health?		
1. Personal unfolding	5.1	3.4
2. Good morale	19.5	9.0
3. Joy of living	14.6	22.3
4. Equilibrium	30.7	19.6
5. Top of one's form	25.4	44.7
No answers	4.7	1.0

Table XII: The themes of health and the global percentages of the answers by CHOICES from 11,000 respondents of the Centre de Médecine Préventive in 1978 and the 3,000 respondents in Nijmegen.

10 of the 18 items were borrowed literally from the list of the 41 fundamental themes. which were regrouped into 10 rubrics in Table I. The other 8 items that remain take up, in a synthetic manner, the main ideas of the 31 other themes, sometimes complementing them (for example that of leisure).

The first impression that emerges in reading the results of Table XII is the **resemblance** in the variations of scores obtained in the two regions for the 18 items.

A second observation has to do with the smaller proportion of non-respondents in Nijmegen than in Nancy.

A third remark concerns the disparity of percentages obtained from certain items between the two cities: these are available in Table XIII.

DEFINITIONS OF HEALTH	PERCENTAGES of the DIFFERENCES between NIJMEGEN and NANCY
1. Precautions	- 14.2
2. Equilibrium	- 11.1
3. Good morale	- 10.5
4. Work	- 2.0
5. Personal unfolding	- 1.7
6. To know oneself well	- 1.4
7. To have luck	- 1.2
8. Not to feel one's body	+ 0.7
9. Leisure	+ 2.0
10. Physical resistance	+ 3.0
11. To be able to face all problems	+ 4.2
12. To feel well in one's skin	+ 5.6
13. Not to be sick	+ 7.0
14. Medicine	+ 7.4
15. Joy of living	+ 7.7
16. Hygiene	+ 14.1
17. Good living and working conditions	+ 19.1
18. Top of one's form	+ 19.7

Table XIII: Classification of definitions of health according to the order of their differences between Nancy and Nijmegen from the most negative (-) to the most positive (+).

One notes that 8 items show small variations (from - 2 % to + 4.2 %); 4 items have average variations in the positive sense (from + 5.6 % to 7.7 %); 6 have variations higher than 10 %, of which 3 in the negative sense and 3 in the positive.

The three themes that vary in diminishing significantly from Nancy to Nijmegen are *precautions* (- 14.2 %), *equilibrium* (- 11.1 %) and *good morale* (- 10.5 %).

The three themes that vary even more strongly in increasing from Nancy to Nijmegen concern *hygiene* (+ 14.1 %), *conditions of living and working* (+ 19.1 %) and *top of one's form* (+ 19.7 %).

Where do these fluctuations of a third of the items come from? Undoubtedly, it is a question of translation, with the Dutch equivalents of the French terms not having necessarily a similar semantic contents.

Nevertheless, beyond the very clear disparities of the two cities, we would like to show, in the last table, their more radical similarity, though it is less easily perceptible: a socio-economic structure very close to each other emerging from the data of the two investigations.

3. A Similar Socio-Economic Structure

In Table XIV, we have represented Nancy with the capital letter "A" and Nijmegen with "E", in such a way that the predominance of a grouping of themes in the same SEC for the two cities is expressed by the two joint letters "Æ".

We see that 6 themes predominate in the higher and middle class: *hygiene, equilibrium, not to feel one's body, personal unfolding, to feel well in one's skin, good living and working conditions*.

At the other extremity of the class structure, manual workers who are the least favored, share the same predominance in defining health as *work, non-sickness*, and *luck*.

Among the higher class, one sees in addition to the 6 themes mentioned above, and in common with the employees, the themes *to know oneself well*. Thus a total of 7 themes on that side.

Among manual workers, one can add to the three previous ones *top of one's form, to be able to face all problems, precautions* and, in common with employees, *physical resistance, joy of living, medicine*. Thus 9 themes on that side.

Definitions of Health	S.E.C.					
	higher Class	middle class	employees	qualified workers	specialized workers	service employees
1. Hygiene	Æ	E				
2. Equilibrium	Æ	E				
3. Not to feel one's body	Æ	E				
4. Personal unfolding	Æ	A				
5. To feel well in one's skin	Æ	Æ				
6. Living and working conditions	Æ	Æ				
7. Leisure	Æ		E	E		E
8. To know oneself well	E	Æ	E			
9. Good morale	E	E		A	A	A
10. Medicine			Æ	E	E	E
11. Physical resistance			Æ	E		
12. Joy of living			E	A	E	E
13. Precautions				Æ	Æ	Æ
14. To be able to face all problems				Æ	E	Æ
15. Top of one's form				E	Æ	E
16. Work					Æ	E
17. Not to be sick					Æ	E
18. To have Luck					Æ	E

Table XIV: The variations of the 18 definitions of health according to socio-economic category in Nancy (A) and in Nijmegen (E): classification according to the percentages of Nancy.

There remain two themes whose socio-economic distribution show a certain discordance in the two European regions:

- *leisure,* more specific to the higher class in Nancy, is also a preoccupation among employees and qualified workers in Nijmegen
- *good morale,* which is more frequent among manual workers in Nancy, is, by contrast, more frequent among the higher class in Nijmegen.

In other words, in spite of a stricter limitation of the number of themes in close-ended questions (18) by comparison with the list of themes in the open-ended question (41), one finds again the scalar structure seen in Table I and II with the interpretation we have suggested of a **double polarity** in the image of health: at one extremity variations of health as more *positive*, more appropriated, more egocentric, to health as more *negative*, more alienated, more sociocentric at the other extremity.

4. Conclusion

This succinct presentation in the five tables leads us to consider a double convergence:

- one is *methodological* and concerns the two processes of research that are the open-ended and the close-ended questions
- the other, of a *geographic* order, is that of two regions of the European Union comprising resemblances and differences that would be too long to enumerate here.

And certainly, our research has also limits that should be elaborated: the cognitive aspects are more developed than the affective and emotional aspects of health.

Nevertheless, as they have been sketched in these few pages, our three investigations lead to a realization of a variation in the image of health as a function of the roles of the respondents in the economic system: the role of *mastery* among the higher classes, the role of *execution* for the manual worker.

And yet, nothing permits us to pose, nor to exclude, a causal relationship between these variations of the image of health and those of the social inequalities of health, from which we started. We can only acknowledge the parallel nature of the two series of variations. These we should seek to explain through further investigations.

RECAPITULATION OF PART II

a) In Chapter 3, starting with 4,000 responses to an open-ended question on the best definition of health, we asked ourselves what were the representations of health in the population. In order to test the methodology of a psycho-social research susceptible to provide an answer to that question, a trial was realised with a sample of the Lorraine population who underwent a health check-up: an open-ended question on the best definition of health has, from 1971 to 1974, produced among 4,000 informants 6,172 response elements, which were classified along 41 principal themes (or definitions) and these were then logically regrouped in 10 synthetic themes (or groups of definitions).

Using the parameter of socio-economic (or occupational) category, the one that revealed itself to be most pertinent, we observed a scalar distribution of definitions of health. It then appears that the image of health, more negative and more socialised among manual workers, more positive and more personalised among higher socio-economic strata, varies with the roles of individuals according to the tasks that society requires them to perform.

b) In chapter 4, starting with the responses of 11,000 respondents to five self-administered close-ended questions (of 2 to 4 or 5 items each), a second investigation carried out in 1978, took up with the aid of 4 close-ended questions the most important of the 41 themes that emerged from the open ended question. Two close ended questions each proposed five of these definitions aimed at defining precisely what is health according to the respondents. Two other close-ended questions of 4 themes each synthesised the main contents of the other previous definitions with a common perspective: where does health come form? A fifth close-ended question was aimed at uncovering fatalistic and non-fatalistic tendencies of the respondents in the four previous questions.

The results shown here lead to a scalar structure going from the most positive and the most egocentric to the most negative and the most socio-centric, the latter being more concentrated among the more fatalistic informants. The distributions according to socio-economic category are, as they were in the first research, such that the cadres or upper-level managers or professionals locate themselves more on the positive, egocentric, non-fatalistic pole and manual workers more on the negative, socio-centric and fatalistic pole. The correspondences according to age are such that, for the main representations of health, the younger generations rejoin the position of the cadres and the older generations those of the manual workers, with the most important themes sometimes bringing together the elderly and the cadres or the younger ones and the manual workers.

A comparison of the results of that second inquiry (with close-ended questions) with the first (with an open-ended question) reveals, beyond some notable divergences due to differences in sampling and in methodology, a convergence of the main tendencies resumed here.

c) In chapter 5, we presented the results of a study that compared the Nancy population with that of Nijmegen (the Netherlands) in order to provide a cross-national dimension to this research.

Such a comparison shows, first, a strong resemblance in the variation of the scores obtained in the two areas. Second, the proportion of non-respondents was smaller in Nijmegen. Third, there were some important differences in the percentages of certain items which are detailed in the text and which, we feel, may be in part attributable to the question of translation from French into Dutch, as well as semantic differences. On the other hand, the results of the comparative investigation showed a similar socio-economic scalar structure in the responses: the respondents' answers and definitions were to a large extent and in both settings associated with their position in the socio-economic structure and resembled each other.

PART III

HEALTH REPRESENTED
BY ITS SYMBOLS AND ANALOGIES

INTRODUCTION

After having analysed what health represents to our respondents, first in an investigation involving 4,000 persons using an open-ended question, then in a second one this time using close-ended questions with a sample 11,000 persons, and third a study comparing the results of two investigations, one in Nancy, the other in Nijmegen (The Netherlands) also using close-ended questions and choices, we now propose, in that Part III, to explain what health means to a population starting from the verbal materials of the answers.[a]

In the next three chapters, we shall seek to analyse and to comment the symbolic representations underlying themes or notions in which respondents have identified health, in focusing more particularly on variations according to age and according to socio-occupational category (see ch. 3 and 4; for more details, particularly on age, see d'Houtaud, 1976 and 1977a).

To this end, we shall take up once more, and we shall deepen, successively: what is the role of the body in representations of health (Ch. 6); the what health is when it is expressed in prevention, hygiene, equilibrium, vitality (Ch. 7); then what is health expressed as non-sickness, well-being, pleasure, value (Ch. 8).

At last, we shall complete this psychosociological itinerary with a more synthetic reflection on the social representation of health as a mirror of the human being and of its social environment (Ch. 9).

---

[a] The reader should also refer to the works of CL. Herzlich (1973 and 1979), to the attempts at synthesis of M. Stacey (1976 and 1978), taken up more recently by R. Williams (1983) and by M. Calnan (1987). Many presentations were the subject of a colloquium held in Nijmegen in July 1984 (Tax, 1984) and in a recent book published by C. Currer and M. Stacey (1986).

Chapter 6

The Body and Health

1. Presentation of Themes

In the open-ended questions, five themes refer, directly or indirectly, to the body : four of these were taken up in the close-ended questions (cf. Table XV).

Globally, **references to the body** are more frequent in the close-ended questions than in the open-ended ones. *To be at the top of one's form* and *to be able to work* remain stable, whereas *to feel well in one's skin* is mentioned almost five times more often in the close-ended question as in the open-ended one, *not to feel one's body* being mentioned more than three times less.

To be at the top of one's form dominates among manual workers and among the youngest, whereas work is most frequently mentioned among manual workers and the oldest ones.

THEMES	QUESTIONS	
	OPEN-ENDED	CLOSE-ENDED
1. *Not to feel one's body*	2.7	0.8
2. *To feel well in one's skin*	2.5	10.4
3. *A healthy mind in a healthy body*	1.2	-
4. *To be at the top of one's form*	6.5	6.4
5. *To be able to work*	2.4	2.4
Totals	15.3	20.00

Table XV: Themes referring to the **body**: comparison of frequencies in open and close-ended questions.

2. To be at the Top of One's Form

The expression *to be at the top of one's form* is most often mentioned in the language of sportsmen or people who refer to models of sports[b]. Its application is thus chiefly physical: it is the good exertion of the body that is intended. There is a reference to a lasting experimentation, to a psych-osocial interpretation of physiological data. Such an interpretation relates subjective phenomena to external objectives: performance in sports, for those who devote themselves to it and, in other fields of activities, for those who like to compare themselves to those who are sportsmen. The psycho-social nature of the interpretation comes from the advantage that speakers find in comparing themselves to others by passing for sportsmen: the comparison is seen as flattering.

3. Work

In the previous definition of health, the **body** was valued through its relation to a social use [c]. Among the younger generations, this is more prized than the other physical activity that is manual work, and which is more characteristic of the older generation [d] up to the cessation of work. Already in ancient civilizations, Greek for example, physical work was the exclusive lot of slaves or servants, i. e., of subordinate categories of society. In the Jewish book of Genesis, it is presented as divine punishment following original sin. As slaves were gradually promoted to the level of humans and as slavery was finally eliminated. Christianity made of work a means of redemption, of salvation.

The most paradoxical end-result of this evolution has been the well-known affirmation, at the beginning of a song: *work is health.* This affirmation became more and more valid in the measure that idleness acquired the reputation as the mother of all vices. In our days, by

---

[b] See M.Bouet (1968). This work develops on the subject of sport numerous themes which cross-cut those we use with respect to health : we cannot here establish a complete parallelism. Let us note nonetheless the hygienic function of sport (cf : the role of medical gymnastics, pp. 268-288, 471-477 ; and, in Sweden, the role of fencing in the movement in favor of health, page 354) ; its functions as leisure (pp. 529-588), professionals (pp. 569-572). Just like health, sport contains religious aspects (pp. 237-364), naturistic (p.265), hedonist (pp.271 and 467).

[c] See the fundamental article by L. Boltanski (1971) on this theme and its critical presentation in chapter 22 of our work (d'Houtaud, 1971).

[d] For them, more than for the younger ones, health is a means to work. In this case health is defined by results. One should note the often painful and sometimes dangerous character of certain manual occupations.

contrast, as a result of the progressive mechanization of repetitive tasks, then of their automation, man acquires again a disponibility for leisure (the *otium* of the Latins). In our industrial society, the most prized physical activity is less and less manual labor which is often left to salaried immigrants (cf: the continuation of the song above: *to do nothing is to conserve* it (health); or the formula: *the less we do the better we are*. But, as in the past or at all times, in the privileged social categories, this physical activity is that of sport.

4. Of Sport and Sexual Connotations

Sport presents itself more like a personal game than a social obligation. It is the free disposition of the body for personal aims, almost playful ones, not its subjection to collective demands (work, war). It can however become a kind of obligation as it is for professional players. *To be at the top of one's form* or *full form* is thus a quality that makes the body available for a type of disinterested activity, where the sentiment of liberty, even of creativity and gratuity, is stronger than constraints: man tends to express himself like a god. Once his body is liberated, he realizes his personal aspirations. In sum, only a minority speak of health as *being able to work*: a much greater number speak of it as the full form, *to be at the top of one's form*.

Is one justified to discern in that full form, as in sport, another connotation: that of power in general and of sexual power in particular[(e)]? It is not accidental if the human being liberates his body from exacting and tiring tasks and simultaneously claims, in certain civilizations, to emancipate himself from certain taboos relating to sex. **Sexual life** has become a social symbol of the conquest of the personality in the same title as the exercise of physical aptitudes in sport. Its playful aspect is also undeniable. Sexual life, like sport, tends to institute a relationship with someone else. Less and less subordinated to procreation, sexuality is sought more and more for its personal and psycho-social aspects. The satisfactions of the libido lend themselves well, among those who seek them, to the pleasures of sharing. In this respect, sexual activity is capable of founding a *familial cell*, just as sport activity creates a *team*. In the two instances however,

---

(e) See again M. Bouet (pp. 467-471), the *hedonistic function* of sport : "It is the essentially corporal and sensitive enjoyment, experienced in the flesh itself of man. Sport is one of the forms where man experiences pleasure in his carnal being (p. 467). And it is "in the sphere of exalted vitality, in the power of emerging life, that it introduces us to regenerate us" (pp. 468-469). And the author cites Nietzsche : "All the healthy functions of the organism have that need and every organism is an ensemble of systems that struggle to increase its sensations of power" (p. 469).

what each one brings to another could not generally be greater than what he expects to get for himself: as if there were no altruism if not on the basis of a well understood egocentrism, that of the interest that each one normally has in oneself. In sum, assimilated as it is to the full form, health already seems to be tied to the realization of the self, which will however become more manifest in the three following themes relating to the body.

5. Some References to the Body

Under that rubric three expressions or references to the body have been regrouped: *not to feel one's body,* which is most prominent simultaneously among top management and those under 40; *to feel well in one's skin,* which predominates among higher management and those under 50: *a healthy mind in a healthy body,* which is most often cited by top and middle management and those under 50.

6. The Social Use of the Body Among Manual Workers

One finds again the **body** as the locus of sensations and of impressions of well-being: what we can call *physical well-being,* including notably the fact of *feeling well in one's skin,* or being at ease with oneself, then the saying *a healthy mind in a healthy body.* In this respect it is to be noted that the full form, or *to be at the top of one's form,* an expression that is current in the sport world, is not predominant among management but is among manual workers; it is parallel to work, the other use of the body, but its social use equally: and this why we have regrouped these two notions of full forms and of work under the same appellation of physical aptitudes. Among manual workers, the body is thus as *if it were depersonalized and placed into the social circuit,* either in the more utilitarian one of work (f), or in the nobler one of sport: it is the individual who uses his body, but in reference to goals normalised or favored by the group. In this case, health benefits if not exclusively the welfare of the group, at least the welfare of the individual in, by and for the group: the body is not totally the region of the self, as it is among higher management in the

---

(f)   The peasant family is an instrument of solidary work, where individual illness constitutes a perturbation of the enterprise, whereas the working class family includes sometimes several workers, but independent each from the other in work: in this case, illness affects only the solidarity of incomes.

expression *to feel well in one's skin* (cf: the German distinction between *Leib* and *Körper*).

Let us note, all the same, in what way, although differently in **work** and in **sport**, is the body used to define health. At the pole of physical activities, neither health nor the body is promoted, truly and only for itself. They take the value of instruments: in work, in the service of earning one's daily bread, in sport very frequently in the service of a team or a collectivity. Undoubtedly, one can see in the definition of health as physical aptitudes the survival, at the lower end of the social ladder, of what had been the absolute priority in the course of previous millennia: to survive through physical strength in hunting, in war as in work. Health and body were united in the service of the instinct of conservation of individuals, and, even more, of the species. Indeed, the body is a precious and remarkable tool: health is nothing else beside its unproblematic functioning, without serious incident; or, according to the remark of R. Leriche, its silence. The body and health are as if recuperated for superior ends at the service of which, just like individuals, they must place themselves unconditionally.

7. The Body at the Service of the "I" Among Managers (Cadres)

Completely different is the reference to the body among managers or cadres. Their promotion and their emancipation in social life involve that of the body and of health. And beside, the contribution of managers or cadres to the work of society is more mental than physical, more intellectual than physiological. What to do of that body thus rendered available? One solution would be to forget it, to place it in parentheses, eventually to put it aside, even against its will, in spite of its demands: such an opinion of Manichean origin has strongly marked Judeo-Christian culture and the civilizations of which it was the main inspirer. The other option is to put it at the center of leisure (g) (in sport, certainly, but even more in playful activities) and

---

(g) Such a disponibility was called by the Greeks *sckolé* and by the Romans *otium*. The lack of leisure (*ascholé* and *neg-otium*) has in the end designated commercial activities, novelties then in comparison to arts and traditional techniques : cf Benveniste (1969). Then Cicero designates literary work as *otium literatum*. In the XVIIIth century, J. J. Rousseau speaks of botany done leisurely as an *oiseuse occupation* (a leisurely occupation) in the traditional sense of study (cf : the Greek *sckolé* which has given *scola* and *school*). However, the Encyclopedie which popularizes Christian condemnations (idleness = sin) opposes idleness and leisure together to action, to work : the two are synonyms of laziness, *inertia*.

in personal life (h), being promoted at the margin of the society's requests and of contributions to collective tasks. This is what would explain the *search for feeling good in one's skin*, that of a healthy body as support of a healthy mind, and even the demand of *not feeling one's body*. One could summarize these three expressions referring to the body by the expression, a little bit too ambiguous, of *enjoying one's body*, taken in the sense of *frui* among Latin people. It might be better to speak of the *"I"* that takes possession of the self and finds pleasure in the body. This latter has then less a role of instrument than to **locate the "I" in the living organism**, in order to emerge more and more from nothingness toward being. Health is the quality making it possible to fulfill that function in the promotion of each individual *ego*.

In summary, at the bottom of the social ladder, the body bound to the tasks to which predispose its physical aptitudes or its full form, is only a tool of the *individual toiling inseparably for himself and for society*. At the other end, it is endowed with the aptitude to feel or rather to permit the I to apprehend its existence and the pleasure to thus be in its body. And such appear the two poles between which individuals oscillate according to the influence, more or less decisive, of the groups to which they belong.

8. Recapitulation

The analysis of themes, evoking directly or indirectly the body in the definition of health, reveals two great orientations that are relatively in the responses, whether to open- or close-ended questions:

- a manifestation, beyond the image of health, of the most profound representations concerning the self
- and, in this overtaking of the perception of health by that of the self, a socio-occupational differentiation of representations having to do with corporal or physical activities.

However, these two orientations emerge clearly only at the stage of the interpretation of the comparisons instituted between the unequal insistence of ones and others on the different notions utilized to speak of health, starting from direct or indirect references to the body or of its activities.

(h)   In the past, what could a nobleman do when he was not at war ? Love, hunting... Has not the word *game* (jeu) signified also coitus ? (Cf : Marivaux : the game of love and chance).

At this stage, among the respondents, health appears as experienced in the midst of the exercise of corporal or physical activities: it is less a question of perceived as of *lived health.*

In the next chapter, we shall speak of evocations of health that imply, on the part of the respondents, going beyond the lived experience through an access to *perceived health.*

Chapter 7

Health in Prevention, Hygiene, Equilibrium, Vitality

1. Presentation of the Themes

In exploiting the responses to an open-ended question, we regrouped all the answers dealing with the problems of *prevention, hygiene, equilibrium* and *vitality*. In the close-ended questions, we only took up the three first ones of these notions taken globally, and we took from the fourth one the two themes of *personal unfolding* and the *ability to face all problems of the future* (cf. Table XVI).

THEMES	QUESTIONS	
	OPEN	CLOSED
1. *Prevention*	14.7	7.3
2. *Hygiene*	12.4	13.6
3. *Equilibrium*	15.4	7.7
4. *Vitality*	4.1	4.7
Totals	46.5	33.3

Table XVI: Themes referring to perceived health: comparison of frequencies in open and close-ended question.

At the global level, this group of themes receives, in the two studies, substantively different frequencies: 46.5% and 33.3%.

Whereas *hygiene* and *vitality* benefit from a certain stability, *prevention* and *equilibrium* are mentioned half as many times in the close-ended question as in the open-ended ones.

2. Prevention

In close-ended questions, prevention was proposed in a global manner. On the other hand, in an open-ended question, it was the object of a series of responses which would, it seems to us, be worthy of a rapid examination [a].

The definitions of health in reference to **prevention** constitute 14.7 % of the mentions of the 4,000 respondents. It is, in the importance of the percentages of the 6,000 elements of responses, the second grouping, behind that of *equilibrium*. It regroups five themes, whose least frequent are: *to live as long as possible* (0.4%) which appears particularly among employees (0.9%) and workers (0.7%) and which is more the aspiration of those under 30 (0.6%); *it is better to prevent than to cure* (1.8%), a response that is particularly dominant among workers (2.3%). among those 40-49 (2.1%) and those 50-59 (2.8%).

The three other definitions have comparable frequencies: *to undergo a health check-up regularly* (4.3%),which is mentioned by the workers (7%) and even more by agricultural workers (9.7%), which partially rejoins those 40-49 (5%) and particularly those 50-59 (6.4%); *to watch oneself* (4.2%) which is particularly the concern of those 50 to 59 (57%) and which one sees specially among employees (5%), among urban and rural manual workers; *to know oneself well* (4%), which is clearly the concern of those in agriculture (5.8%) and more than anyone else among those 60 and over (7.1%).

In the close-ended questions, we examined again only: *to know oneself well*, which appears but lightly among the middle classes, more strongly among those 40 and over; *to take precautions* which is strongest among specialized workers and service personnel, and less marked among those over 40.

The request for *a regular health check-up* is natural for a population that just underwent one and at a time when, after having been legislated in 1945, it is not sought any more only by heads of private enterprises concerned with the future of their cadres: on the contrary, in our sample, it is demanded before all by manual workers, specially rural ones.

(a) Let us recall that 100 % of the 6, 000 elements of response on the part of the 4, 000 respondents were distributed in 41 themes, assembled into 10 groupings of themes. Hence the smallness of the percentages in each one of the 41 themes.

One could, by the way, wonder why agricultural workers are more enclined toward *prevention*, and more particularly a health check-up. Does this come from their being more influenceable by the check-up to which they have just been subjected? However they are equally more desirous than the others to know themselves well. Does this come then from the fact they are recruited more from among those over 40, where the two themes of the *health check-up* and to *know oneself well* predominate? Whatever the answer, rurals appear more inclined toward precautions: it is one of the earmarks of peasant mentality, whose tasks must be organized as a function of the seasonal rhythms in agriculture or the biological rhythms in animal husbandry and which must take into account, as part of its resources, the hazards of the weather.

The attitudes of prevention that are met, certainly, all along the life course, become more intense after the age of forty, and more and more as the individual becomes older. Is it, at the level of comportments, the echo of a certain diffuse fear intensified by the approach of old age and its precursor signs, or the effect of some difficult experiences with illness, already seen as warnings? In any case, we shall see when dealing with non-sickness (in the next chapter) that these same groups of people also want to be seen regularly by a physician.

In the grouping of prevention, a rapprochement imposes itself between to *know oneself well* and *to watch oneself*. In the two instances, health is explicitly tied to attitudes, more or less egocentric, of observation and even of introspection. This signifies, in particular, that health here is defined through the activities of which it is the object, i. e. through the preoccupation to discover oneself. Which also means that, from the moment when one is preoccupied with observing oneself, one will detect more easily all the anomalies that are susceptible to alter a pre-existing health. Don't we say: *who knows himself, is feeling well?* It is a transposed version of the Socratic notion: *know yourself* (*gnoti seauton*), recentered here in a very utilitarian way on the object of feeling well, of being healthy.

3. Hygiene

According to Greek legend. **Hygiè,** daughter of Asclepios (of whom the Roman made Aesculapius), is the goddess of health(cf. Ch.1). The Greek term *Hugiaino* means, first, to feel well, to be in good health. One would not be able to find a term whose etymological origins refer so explicitly to health in general. Nevertheless, in English and in French, the term has more and more oriented itself toward a meaning of what conditions health within a framework of daily life, of work, of housing and of leisure.

In close-ended questions, the notion of **hygiene**, taken in a global fashion, clearly predominates among higher management and those under 50. Under this theme we have regrouped, in the exploitation of the open-ended question, 12.4% of the responses: more precisely, ten notations going from 2.5% to 0.4%. Two of these have a frequency superior to 2%: *a regular life* (2.5%) which emerges among the non-active (3.4%), particularly women at home and aged persons and among employees (2.7%); *a healthy life* (2.4%), to which workers more than anyone else aspire (2.8%); these two notations predominate among those 60 years and over (4.9% and 3.5% respectively).

Between 1% and 2% one meets: *not to make excesses* (1.8%). which is a preoccupation of urban manuals (2.3%) and rural manuals (2.7%), as well as those 60 and over (3.5%); *to have a balanced diet.* noted particularly by employees (2%) and those under 30 (1.8%) ; *to engage in sport,* more marked among workers (1.2%) and those under 30 (1.3%). Of the other five notations (from 0.8% to 0.4%). three predominate among urban dwellers: *to have a good appetite, to live as long as possible in the open air, to sleep well; sobriety* is common to manual workers, particularly rural; *to rest* is the aspiration of workers, particularly, those 60 and over.

In the open-ended question, the insistence of older persons on four of these themes (*regular life, active life, no excesses, to rest*) proves that it is, in part, a question of very general attitudes of hygiene, reflecting the mentality of people who fear incidents of health: the formulations themselves refer back to a life experience. The idea shared in common is to use with regularity, if not parsimony, that health whose reserves from now on are revealed as limited: would too numerous or too strong excesses (or irregularities) not compromise that health to which is so closely tied the survival of many aged persons? For the dominant preoccupation of these persons is not so much of living than simply surviving: one feels among these persons a more marked anxiety in the presence of problems to resolve from day to day. In these problems health is the decisive ace in the hole, permitting them to face these problems, to confront them in a more favorable position.

The four attitudes of hygiene that characterize the youngest are very different. For them what matters is *to have a balanced diet, a good appetite, to engage in sport, to sleep well.* Together, they constitute the basic conditions of development, of expansion: it is a question before all of activity (sport) and what restores strength after activity (appetite, food, sleep). Here, what is important is to live fully, to spend without counting, to go resolutely forward, toward well-being or surpassing oneself.

In any case, it is not accidental that *hygiene* is more the demand of urban workers (15.7%) and employees (13.3%) than those in the rural areas (9.1%) or even higher management (9.4%). For is not hygiene the required counter-thrust to urbanization with its concentrations of populations where housing and factories are cheek-by-jowl, where infectious diseases spread more easily because of a greater human density and a greater promiscuity? At any rate, hygiene calls more for personal initiatives that are assiduously repeated: they suppose individuals persuaded of its merits, conscious of the risks to which too sedentary an existence exposes them, as well as too artificial an alimentation, and residential areas lacking fresh air and invaded by noise. Furthermore, the terms brought together under the rubric of hygiene reflect, very closely, those than the mass media diffuse, whose impact is more visible in the town that in the countryside. Is it not significant that those in agriculture are predominant in this sector only to advocate not to engage in excesses or to be sober, but they do not even feel the need to speak spontaneously of their appetite, of their sleep, of sport?

4. Equilibrium (15.4%)

When it comes to *prevention* and to *hygiene*, we have had less opportunity to encounter, in an open-ended question, members of management or cadres (and yet there are 2,142 higher and middle management persons among the 4,000 respondents). This comes from the fact that the notations of these two groupings of definitions constitute 35.8% of the elements of responses from workers, 31.1% of those of rural workers, 27.2% of those of employees, but only 21.5% of those of middle management and 22.2% of those of higher management.

On the contrary, the grouping of **equilibrium,** which holds the first place in the mentions of the totality of respondents (15.4%), reaches only 7.6% of those of the workers, 9.7% of those in agriculture, 15.3% of those of employees, but it climbs to 19.9% of those of higher management. This shows how much this grouping is complementary to the two previous ones. All three are such that they can be associated in a same perspective: that of the conditions of access to health and its maintenance.

This high frequency of the theme has permitted us to distinguish the use of the substantive (*equilibrium)* with or without qualifiers (physical, mental or familial).

With the exception of *equilibrium in the family,* which is named twice as often by those in agriculture (2.6%) as among higher management (1.3%), the other qualifiers of *equilibrium* are very weak among urban and rural manual workers. The distinction between *physical* and *mental* is particularly made by managers, especially higher managers (from 9% to 10% of their total mentions). From the viewpoint of age, that distinction predominates among those under 30 (almost 7% of their total mentions), while remaining strongly affirmed among those 50-59 (more than 6%). The *good equilibrium*, used without reference to the mental or physical, predominates from the age of 50, whereas *equilibrium within the family* characterizes particularly those 40-59, precisely those most concerned by their family responsibilities.

By contrast, in the close-ended questions, *equilibrium* has been introduced without its sub-themes. It remains, nevertheless, the apanage of higher management (double of what is seen among specialized workers), and those under 40.

Few informants, undoubtedly, who utilize the term of equilibrium to define health, have an idea of its etymological meaning: *equal balance*. Two notions underlie the usual sense of the term: forces oppose each other; they exert themselves in such a way as to produce a durable state of rest or movement. One speaks not only of a static equilibrium, but also a dynamic one. In the current meaning, the human body can hold itself standing up, vertically, maintain that stance while walking or riding a bicycle: in the two cases, it remains in equilibrium; in the contrary case, it loses that equilibrium.

By analogy, one speaks of a budgetary equilibrium, of the balance of payments of a country, of the balance of powers in a constitution or among states or blocs of nations. In a more banal way, a person is said psychologically or affectively balanced: thus mental equilibrium has differentiated itself from physical equilibrium. In sum, to speak of equilibrium means to evoke a harmony between tendencies in activity and in adaptation: a human being passes for equilibrated or balanced in his professional and family activities or in his adaptation to new functions.

To compare health to equilibrium is equivalent, consequently, to imagine the body and the mind as fields where forces are deployed in such a manner that they procure that element of balance or stability that permits them to operate effectively. In this case, one speaks of a state of health, either stable or aggravated: is this the main origin of the references made by the respondents to equilibrium? Is there not equally the sentiment that the organism is the theater, where forces face each other and over which the individual has no control, but on which his health depends? If a disequilibrium should appear, then one resorts to the ministrations of a therapist to help restore that equilibrium, without which health and sometimes life itself are compromised.

The notion of equilibrium can also be understood in relation to that of excess: one must eat and drink in moderation. It is the same in all physical activities where also a certain moderation is desirable.

For one's health, one seeks alimentary moderation, an equilibrium in work and in sport. The end being assimilated to the means, one brings health back to an equilibrium.

One can also explain such an assimilation through the representation of the struggles that every organism must sustain against the trials and the dangers of its environment, in particular against the threat of epidemics, accidents at work and on the road. If microbes or viruses compromise the usual equilibrium of organs and tissues, it is advisable to reestablish it with adapted antidotes or medications. The surgical intervention is felt more as a source of disequilibrium, unless it is a question of extirpating a more serious source of disequilibrium (a tumor, for example). This is why health is lived as a precarious equilibrium, constantly threatened, but which in close-ended questions predominates, either because of luck, or the resistance of the organism, or from precautions.

One can also understand by equilibrium the interior harmony of the individual, notably between his physical and his mental reality. Or as a harmony of the forces of the living being with those of its environing milieu. Or even as a somewhat vague substitute, at the health level, of the notion of order at the social level: the coordination of all organs and tissues or that of all social classes and occupations, produces a homogeneous global reality, stable, efficacious. One thinks naturally of the analogy between the physical and the social corps, a particularly well developed analogy in Christian culture of the church as a corporate entity.

The equilibrium is also the inherent property of a world conceived among the Greeks as a cosmos, i. e., as a harmonious universe. In the same way, equilibrium is a key-notion in the world of machines and economic exchanges: more or less of military origins (the equilibrium of forces facing each other), it is more and more applied to the relations of political forces.

Taken at a very general level, the term equilibrium is used, classically, to characterize either vital exchanges between the cell or the organism and their milieu, or the relations of forces between individuals or between groups. Nothing is more expressive of a conception simultaneously conquering, measured or mastered in health: a tendency that rejoins the general orientations of higher classes or management.

Even if the notion of equilibrium appears more complex at the level of interpretation than of prevention, the fact is that it predominates in the most favored social strata of modern societies, i. e. those least inclined to define health by prevention or even hygiene, Thus there is every reason to locate equilibrium as representing, in its extreme form, people who are most favored, something that is equivalent of hygiene and prevention at the other extreme, of those who are the most disadvantaged.

If such is the case, health would then be perceived and represented as equilibrium in proportion to the degree of integration of individuals in the cultural and social life of a country. Hence the insistence of higher classes or cadres on this definition and, by contrast, the reserve of those classes that are managed, directed or ordered, i. e. workers, for example.

From that vantage point, in contrast with the conceptions of the higher classes, the means envisaged by manual workers and employees appear negative: *prevention* and *hygiene*. In the two cases, the socio-professional axis of the most important percentages is constituted by workers, to whom are added, in second position, those in agriculture for prevention, and employees for hygiene. In prevention, the insistence of those in agriculture comes from their demand to go through a health examination regularly; in hygiene, that of employees comes above all from the demands for a regular life and balanced diet. It is, at that level, seemingly, two substitutions to the notion of *equilibrium* dear to the higher classes.

Health, thus conceived as precaution, is not so much any more to be attached to the sphere of personal unfolding as to another sphere, that one where there appears the subordination of the individual to society or to fate. For those who are not in the higher classes, health is perceived as a function of the scientific possibilities of the society in a specific era: it is health endured, protected against the risks of the environment.

In this sense, a certain bi-polar structuration of the definitions of health appears characteristic of those societies that have hierarchical bi-polar structures: the pole of the most favored and those least advantaged by social life.

5. Vitality

The last grouping that remains to be presented is also the weakest: 4.1% of the mentions by the respondents in an open-ended question, but 6% of these among middle managers, on the one side, 2.6% among workers and 2.4% among those in agriculture. It is a matter of five themes, that we have designated under the common title of **vitality** (or expansion): *to be able to face all problems, not to be afraid of the future,* as well as *personal unfolding, optimism* and *dynamism.* Indeed, higher management are, above all, interested in dynamism. However, the socio-occupational axis of this group consists of middle management, whose employees are near to *optimism* and to *face all problems.*

In the close-ended questions we have taken up but two of these five themes. They have obtained a percentage (4.7%) superior to that of the five themes in the open-ended question (4.1%), *to face all problems of life* (3.4%), *unfolding* (1.3%). If the second clearly predominates among higher classes (twice that of workers) and those under 40 (the double of those 60 and over), the first one predominates among service personnel and those 40 to 60.

One can bring this theme close to that of *not being afraid of the future* where, in the open-ended question, middle management detach themselves from other categories. One cannot, by the same token, place health in relation to its *salutary* function, its role as purveyor of survival. Its connivance with the ambivalent time (simultaneously creator and destructor of life) which brings out one of two eventual values: that which assures to the living their temporal salvation, although always provisionally and precariously. And hence the optimism that results from it, that of the middle managers (1.3%) and employees (1.1%), that of those 50-59 (1.5%) and those over 60 (1.1%) i. e. a vision of the future such that one expects something better than what the present brings: health creates that expectation, makes it a reality.

There remain in this grouping two other definitions of health: *dynamism* and *personal unfolding* (or blooming). These are two themes tied to the expansion of the *ego*, to that of individual personality sufficiently developed and socially affirmed to be in position to hope even more.

The grouping of these five definitions (to which we hesitated to add that of *to live as long as possible,* finally classified in the prevention grouping) seemed to us difficult be unify under a single appellation. Finally we chose *vitality,* in order to express a kinship and a continuity with the grouping of *the hedonistic use of life* which will discuss in the next chapter. Thus vitality is an expression of the individual will to live.

6. Recapitulation

Starting from the data of our investigations, one with an open-ended question having obtained from 4,000 respondents about forty themes to define health, the other by close-ended questions having obtained from 11,000 respondents their reactions to about twenty of the previous themes, we have sought, in a first study, to analyse the role of the body in their representations of health. In that second chapter of Part III, we have touched upon the means utilized to accede to health and to maintain oneself with it.

Having done so, we sketched a kind of itinerary **from health as lived to health as perceived**. Indeed to characterize health by expressions such as *not to feel one's body, to feel well in one's skin*, or through the saying *a healthy mind in a healthy body* or through evoking the full form or physical labor, constitutes indeed a call to what is being lived, to an empirical given, to which one certainly refers, but whose implications one does not seek to elucidate. By contrast, to define health in resorting to attitudes or behaviors of prevention and hygiene or to the even more elaborate notion of equilibrium, is to locate oneself at a more critical level. It is the one where one perceives health through realizations in which one has the initiative and where one feels able to seek it for itself. Such is the sense of the title under which we thought to regroup the reflections inspired by part of the verbal materials obtained from numerous respondents, examined according to their age or their socio-occupational category.

Toward the end of this itinery, the question of the underlying representations of health poses itself: this is what we propose to examine in the following chapter, which will consider another part of this verbal material and will attempt to pass from perceived health to represented health.

Chapter 8

Health as Non-Sickness, Well-Being, Pleasure, Value

1. Presentation of the Themes

In the open-ended question (cf. Table XVII), ten themes were regrouped under the three rubrics of *non-sickness* (not to be sick, to be followed by a physician[a]), of *psychological well-being* (joy of living, happiness, good morale, good humor), and of *the hedonistic use of life* (life without constraints, to benefit from life, not to think of sickness, see the physician as little as possible). To that list were added the two themes of the *value of health* (the greatest wealth, the essential).

THEMES	QUESTIONS	
	OPEN	CLOSED
1. Non-sickness	11.7	20.6
2. Psychological well-being	11.8	8.6
3. The hedonistic use of life	7.4	12.5
4. The value of health	7.2	-----
Totals	38.1	41.7

Table. XVII: Themes concerning criteria of health: comparison of frequencies in open and close-ended questions.

---

[a] To be under a physician's supervision.

In the close-ended questions, one can similarly regroup four items corresponding to non-sickness (*not to be sick, medicine, physical resistance, good fortune* or *luck*); or find again two of the four notations of psychological well-being (*good morale, joy of living*); two more abstract expressions have played a role similar to that of the hedonistic use of life (*good conditions of life and of work, leisure*).

2. Negative Criteria Of Health

It is a cliché that one does not know health well until it is compromised or lost: "One does not enjoy fully wealth, sleep and health until one has lost them and found them again," wrote J. P. Richter in 1818 in one of his poems. Chauvot de Beauchene seems to echo that observation in his *Maxims, Reflections and Thoughts* (1827) "Health is the most precious treasure and the easiest to lose: it is however the one that is the worst kept." Non-sickness appears in a different guise to R. Leriche: "Health is life in the silence of organs." A notion that Jules Renard expressed in a different fashion in his *Journal* (14 July 1896): "The best health is not to feel one's health." The tendency to define health negatively rejoins the way in which Bichat defined life as the totality of forces that oppose death.

It would be interesting to pursue such an investigation through written works from different eras and countries in order to include them in the results of our investigation: but what we have briefly evoked is enough to manifest, beyond the diversities of situations, certain continuities of attitudes to which writers of the past have contributed to the more recent generations.

At any rate, in choosing a few convergent citations, our intention was to give picturesque or illustrative formulations, complementary one to the other, of what our respondents mean to say when they **define health negatively** by *not being sick* or *to be followed by a physician*. These two definitions dominate among workers, the first one being cited half as often as by high and middle managers.

Curiously, in the open-ended question, non-sickness is more often evoked by those under 30 and resort to a physician among those 40 and over, whereas, in the close-ended question, those 50 and over are more numerous in the two ways of characterizing health.

3. Non-Sickness

It is paradoxical that *not being sick* is mentioned more often by the young in the open-ended question, while morbidity increases with age. Such an attitude can only be considered as a reflection of their concrete situation. Undoubtedly the youngest have, for the most part, only personal experiences of minor sicknesses: protected since childhood from the most dangerous ones through mandatory vaccinations, they have been subjected to the least dangerous ones through precocious exposure. Most often in good health, they observe sickness among their elders. Health, from that viewpoint, afflictions of early infancy aside, is one of the characteristics of the first phases of the human life course: hence the scandal, the anomaly of serious diseases or death among the young for whom health means the essential.

Not being sick or to be under the supervision of a physician have, in common, the use of the notion of the sickness rubric: the opposite of health (the state of non-sickness) or what permits one to verify that state (the social control of the physician). The second formulation consists of saying that one is in good health when the representative of society says so. In the open-ended question, society is virtually taken as an interlocutor: the patient sends back the question to the physician who is qualified, technically and legally, to decide on this question in the name of society.

One can thus verify, once more, the embarrassment humans have in defining positively what health is. At every level, one goes around the obstacle by referring to facts and behaviors. But the question we must answer what are the criteria of achieved and maintained health. It is on this point that the spread appears to be greatest between the two extremities of the social scale in our industrial societies. The first of these **criteria, chiefly negative,** appears above all among workers: *not to be sick* is not mentioned more often by those in agriculture nor by the employees or middle management. As to the second one, *to be seen by a physician,* those in agriculture insist on it along with the workers more markedly than other categories. One recognizes here the importance of the physician for agricultural workers; on the other hand, their distance from the workers on the subject of non-sickness can be explained if one takes into account of the positive role, among them, of criteria of work and full form. Farmers work even when they are sick.

The reference to the state of non-sickness is certainly quite revealing, as mentioned earlier, of the **difficulty of societies to express the positive reality of health.** However, that negative definition is also a revelation of the greater difficulty of manual workers to handle the language tool outside of the techniques and the material tasks they perform. It is typical of individuals whom society utilizes, and whose strengths and time it absorbs: too involved in the social processes of production and consumption, they are not easily capable of critically viewing social realities and abstractions. The worker uses his health much more than he knows how to characterize it for itself. Health is dear to him as it is to anyone else. In particular sickness is feared because of its familial and occupational consequences: even if he does not pay the full price of medical care because of social insurance, it still seems to him expensive. The fact of not being sick is so important a relief to him that it expresses well what health is, that reality that means that under ordinary circumstances all is well.

4. Positive Criteria with Psychological Characteristics

Under this denomination we have associated four other definitions of health (11.8%), which predominate, in the open-ended question, in that category of urban-dwellers who are employees (13.7%) and workers (13.1%), far above higher management (8.5%). One of these themes, *good morale* (2.6%), characterizes more the workers (3.5%). The three others, *joy of living* (5.2%), *happiness* (2.8%), *good humor* (1.2%) predominate among employees (6.1%, 3.3% and 1.6% respectively). In the three cases, let's notice the adjective "good". From the age standpoint, *joy of living* predominates among those 40-49 (5.9%); the three others among those 60 and over: *good morale* (4.2%), *happiness* (3.5%), *good humor* (1.8%).

In close-ended questions, *good morale* is almost four times as frequently mentioned by specialized workers and by service personnel than by higher management and twice as often among those 50 and over than among those under 40. As to *joy of living*, it places employees before all other categories and is found almost twice as often in those under 30 than among those 60 and over.

Globally, *joy of living* goes with youth and lesser morbidity. The three others, which those over 60 cite most often, testify to the good functioning of the organism. They are like a translation, at the psychosocial level, of relationships with others and of occupational or recreational activities. However, *good morale* on the part of "senior citizens" means undoubtedly also the acceptance of disabilities recognized as incurable.

By the same token, one should perhaps see in these definitions an organization that goes hand in hand with urbanization and industrialization. For, in the modern enterprise, the worker is cut off affectively from his work: and, from that point on, his emotional life has other dreams or aspirations that the mass-media strongly encourage to cultivate. However, these criteria are not at all similar to the ways those in agriculture feel. They are manual workers who are more enclined to define health by the full form and even more by work. The average farmer is more interested in the physical workings of his body. The psychological satisfactions of city-dwellers seem too precious to him: they are those of a world to which he is but little attached, and often with which he does not want to be solidary. In this sense, *psychological well-being*, is a transition toward the physical well-being of those more personalized city-dwellers who have become managers: it is the subjectivity placed at the disposal of urban dwellers or a form of introversion that is accepted and consented to by them. It includes a reference to an internal perception of the self that is pleasant, beneficial. It represents a stage in the evolution of the rural man to the "citizen" who is rather searching for personal development (cf ch.7, § 5).

Psychological well-being is, in fact, a lesser social response and already more personal in the sense that it evokes criteria that belong to an introspective perception and to a no less subjective appreciation: *joy of living, happiness, good morale, good humor.* All these elements designate ways of being that are favorable to the subject, attractive to him, thus ways of being at ease with himself: hence the global denomination of *psychological well-being,* in opposition to what will represent, among higher classes or cadres, physical or corporal well-being. For, with respect to those at the bottom of the social scale, the use of the body is still very much oriented toward work or sports, i.e. toward what it produces in (if not for) society. Only the psychological being is appropriated, personalized, really immune to social disposition, at least in appearance: it is the instrument of enjoyment, of good pleasure.

In the four elements of the open-ended question, three predominate among the employees, these for the greater part non-manual city-dwellers (although employees in trade often use their hands: delivery men, postmen, etc; but in our sample those are weakly represented in comparison to office workers, feminine for the most part). The other, by contrast, predominates among workers: *good morale* plays among them the role of the *full form* among agricultural workers. Whereas the full form refers to the body utilized in a voluntarily accepted activity (whose prototype seems to us to be sports), good morale refers us back to the affective tonality that accompanies all activities, notably that of urban manual work that is so little motivating.

If good morale is taken for granted in tasks that interest and passion the subject, it is more problematic where there is a break between the worker and the fruit or the result of his work. Similarly, one experiences all the other activities with or without good morale, according to whether they are or are not the object of a positive emotional investment. In particular, during an illness or medical treatment following a surgical intervention, the patient keeps or loses his good morale: it is generally thought that this morale has great influence on the course of the therapy or on the issue of the illness. And from here to think that work in the urban or industrial milieu is sometimes lived as a sickness or badness there is but one step... (a step implicitly taken by more people than would admit it explicitly).

By contrast, *joy of living, happiness, good humor* are terms that are more smiling, more pleasant, that define health with terms that would fit in the domain of affectivity: love is susceptible of being the cause or the occasion. Health is thus described with sentiments or feelings that appear in happy moments and in terms of an assured value according to our respondents. It is also assimilated to the affective tonality that accompanies it and which becomes a sort of subjectively undoubted confirmation. This is why such signs or internalized criteria of health come more from city-dwellers of modest social standing. Those ones have partially left the objectivism of people from the countryside, which are projected into objects. They have then amplified the dream-like aspects of their interior life, that are so frequently fed by the cinema, the heart-throb press, novels, etc... Health appears to them as an ideal coming from a dream-world to illuminate the zones of individual existence, where everyone likes to take refuge, where he can escape the constraints of professional or occupational life. It is part of the realities of which every human being dreams at the beginning of his life: "the first boon is health, the second is beauty, the third wealth", wrote Plato [b].

5. Positive Criteria with a Hedonistic Character

The response of *non-sickness* is more common among workers than those in agriculture, who are in second position. That of the *psychological well-being* is more common among employees than among workers, who then come in second position. That of the *hedonistic use of life* is found more often among higher classes or cadres.

In fact, this third grouping of definitions (7.4) reaches, in the open-ended question, 10.4 % of the mentions by middle managers and 9.4% of those of higher managers, but only 5,2 % of those of workers and 3.2 % of those in agriculture. Two of these definitions, *life without constraint* (3.4 %), *to profit from life* (2%) predominate equally among those under 30 and those over 60 (4.6 % for one, 2.4 % for the other respectively). The next one, *not to think about illness* (1.3 %), while conserving the same U shape distribution, dominates among those 60 and over (2.2 %). The last one, *to see the physician as little as* possible (0.7%) is not even mentioned among those, but characterizes those under 30 (1%).

---

[b] *Laws.*

In other words, these four objective criteria of health are those of managers: they constitute a group of elements that we have called **the hedonistic use of life**[c]. *See the physician as little as possible* insist higher managers; *to profit from life* prefer the middle managers: the two categories come together to wish for *a life without constraint* (where the higher managers predominate) and *not to think of sickness* (where middle managers predominate).

We also have noted the two negative allusions, one to the physician, more among higher managers than among middle ones, and the other one to illness, more among middle managers, which remains, among both, a kind of lithmus test that has its distant origins in the criteria of the manual workers: the non-illness and the control by the physician. With, however, a fundamental difference: illness is named by the managers only in understatements, just like the physician, whereas manual workers, particularly urban ones, speak frankly of one and the other. They are witness of a certain homogeneity and the continuity of tendencies from one social stratum to another.

Let us note that understatements gather fairly weak percentages compared to negative definitions (cf §2): sickness intervenes in 9 % among middle managers and 11 % among workers, the physician in 2.4 % among higher managers and 7.3 % among workers.

However the two most important mentions (in percentages) of this grouping, among cadres or higher classes, are *life without constraints* and *to profit from life*: they are the ones that, in our view, justify the use of the expression the hedonistic use of life. One reaches there to the most advanced personalization: health is not part of the useful (cf. *uti* among the Latins) as among manual workers when they refer to work and to the full form, but it belongs to enjoyment (cf. the *frui* of the Latins), that of the *ego*, to which personal health and social values are somehow ordered, if not subordinated. Health is placed at the disposal of the pleasure of the individual, who is resolved to obtain a maximum of enjoyment in his life. Here health is not a value in itself (cf. *valere* in ch.1), even less for society, but for the one who benefits from it, who disposes of it at will, profits from it as he wishes to live better, for his own accomplishment and his own destiny.

6. Health as Life Without Constraint

The idea of a **life without constraint** has something mythical: wherever there is life, there are environmental factors to which beings

---

[c] Here *hedonistic* is taken in its philosophical sense : "hedonism has made of pleasure the object to approve of as good... and correlatively of pain the evil to condemn and then to push aside" (R. le Senne, 1942).

must finally adapt if they want to survive; and everywhere there is social organization: individuals must submit themselves to norms, often to laws or conventions. Such constraints are themselves the conditions for the blossoming of individual lives. The demand for freedom intervenes with as much vehemence as does the yearning for life of which it appears as a continuation. Perhaps the informants who have spoken of life without constraint thought first of all of the restrictions imposed upon freedom by illnesses and infirmities: health is recognizable from the fact that none of these constraints weighs on the living being. Nevertheless the general formulation itself bears a meaning that goes well beyond health or that makes of health the symbol of liberated life: on the other hand, that liberated life serves to designate health in a kind of unusual metonymy [d].

Durkheim has utilized the term *constraint* (Bourdieu prefers to speak of *violence*) to designate social pressures on individuals in every group. In its own way, hygiene imposes constraints that are the object of a study by G.L. Duprat)(1930). In reality, the constraints to which every social group subjects its members are the counterpart of the protection that it brings against the scourges of the savage state: in order to be protected from the weather, the hazards of gathering and hunting, predatory animals, enemy clans, epidemics, humans institute services to which everyone is supposed to contribute in his place and time. For, in a hostile world, only the group has the means to survive: *Vae soli* (woe to him who is alone). The more the services of society are differentiated and "sophisticated", the more the individual receives, the more he owes contributions.

The dream of *living without constraint* is less the seeking of an eventual return to natural life as a paradoxical state [e] than it is going beyond the obligations of social life: we have just seen how the classes that are privileged by society are the most tempted by these idyllic representations of life. Is it only a question of utopia? Nothing is less certain, if at least we recognize the distinction according to which, as an individual, the human being is subordinated to society and its realizations, but, as a person, he would be superior to society, which would then be mandated to procure him the means of a complete self-fulfillment. In this sense, to profit or benefit from life represents an advanced stage of personal emancipation with respect to social servitudes: without avoiding these obligations for a part of his self and his life, man aspires to transcend them in order to achieve, in himself, his full self-actualization. Such an approach has already

---

[d] Metonymy is the substitution of an attribute or other suggestive word for the name of the thing meant.

[e] This reproach has often been made to the interpretation of life in society by Ivan Illich.

been proposed by ancient societies, but only to a few privileged social categories.

7. Health as Liberty and License

The attitude of higher classes or cadres is thus entirely realistic: for them health is the hedonistic use of life. Assuredly this statement does not reveal, for the greater part, the non-illness that is just below the surface of what we have called, above, understatements: *not to think of illness, to see the physician as little as possible.* But the essential is elsewhere: *life without constraints, to benefit from life.*

In one part, **health here has the face of freedom**: illness seems the radical constraint, the feared evil. In the literature, illness acts like the plague, like cancer: microbes or viruses are as much synonymous of servitude and subjection as *the Nuées* of Aristophanes or *the Flies* of Sartre [f].

It is as if epidemics and pandemics, as collective realities, opposed themselves to health, a private and individual reality (cf Herzlich, 1979). On the other hand, constraint comes equally from society, from some one else (cf. "hell is the others" in *Huis Clos* by Sartre). And yet, to escape from flies and viruses just like escaping from social contagion or from the world of exile (cf. A. Camus) is to accede to the internal kingdom that is the *ego*: at the same time to health and liberty. Health thus constitutes an integral part of the individual personality: one without the other would be amputated or threatened as it would be without freedom [g].

On the other hand, **health here has equally the face of license**: through it, one draws benefit from life. One would call it a struggle in the course of which it is important to conquer oneself, to realize oneself. The absence or lack of health radically compromises that struggle, in modifying the relationship of forces to the detriment of the "I". Not to be able *to benefit from life* is a little as if one suffered from a handicap, from an infirmity. To be able to benefit from it, is like a gushing out, an exuberance of the self. At any rate, the time of

---

[f] M. Chastain in *La philosophie de Virginia Woolf* (1951) has noted in the work of the English novelist that interpretation tied to illness : "we are all sick. Our afflictions are named suffering, death and, generally, poverty... They appear today to be transmitted by war which affects the entire human race, whereas they were of concern to only a few mercenaries... Its microbes against which our grandparents were vaccinated destroy the certitudes unconsciously elaborated and digested by the spirit of the XIXth century... : they replace them by the disquieting truth of the hour : trenches, cellars, prisons or deportation camps, eroded cities, tortures, murders" (p. 9 cf p. 160).

[g] Proust has, it is true, made from illness an inverse experience (cf. his asthma from youth).

life is counted: every instant that passes without a total life is a defeat, in one part of the *me* that shall be no more and will never have been, a point marked by the destructive time, which will surely vanquish the living and every other living being.

8. Time and Being in Health

Indeed, sickness uses time to corrode the very substance of the *ego:* it is the descent, the fall toward nothingness or the emptiness of death: time applies its function of catastrophe (in the etymological sense of a fall).

The conquering *"I"* is, on the contrary, the recuperated time through a generation of the self to a greater being, to a better being. This passionate search of life for the self and of the self through life is the creator of the *ego*, just like health is the creator of cells, of tissues, of organisms in expansion, in growth. In this sense, life is lived like an impetus toward a maximal and optimal life whose ineluctable consumption is time: hence the haste, the *rage* [h] to live outside of every limit, of every constraint, in one word to want to profit or benefit[i].

Thus, the more the *"I"* becomes conscious of itself, the more it aspires to realize itself in plenitude: it passes then from the recognition of health as *non-sickness* to that of health as *psychological well-being*, then to health as *hedonistic use of life*. In other words, **health is a mirror** where the *"I"* of everyone is reflected: in all cases it sends back to every speaker the hidden face that it harbors within the depth of its desires or its aspirations. Each one knows of health only what he is: he recognizes it through what he prefers in himself.

In sum the hedonistic notations of the open-ended question appear as more concrete and more expressive explanations than the more abstract and somehow shortened formulations of the close-ended questions, when they propose to the respondents that *to have a good health* is to have good conditions of life and of work, and to *remain in good health* comes from leisure activities. Is not access to leisure precisely subordinated to good conditions of life and of work? These constitute favorable environments to those who can escape the constraints of life and to accede to the freedom to realize themselves in full.

---

[h]   See our article (1982).
[i]   In this respect old age appears as a disease.

9. Health as Value

Being present only in the open question, the grouping of the **value of health;** (7.2 %) is highly visible among those in agriculture (10.4 %). In this case exceptionally employees (9.7 %) and even middle managers (7.1 %) are closer to those in agriculture than the workers (6.2 %). With reference to age, the two definitions that constitute this grouping vary separately: the *essential* (3.7 %) regularly diminishes as age increases (from 4.5 % to 2.8 %), whereas the *greatest wealth* predominates among those 60 and over (4.6 %). In other words, the definition where the young clearly predominate, health held as the essential, decreases in the almost inverse proportion of that where health is held as the greatest value.

In the two cases, it is a question of health as a value which, according to the Latin *valere* (= to feel well, to be in good health), it fundamentally is. To examine rigorously the terms, the oldest informants place it as a value more **as to have** (wealth) and the youngest more **as being** (the essential). Should we consider the second formulation as giving more value to the human being? One can ask the question in the measure to which health, reduced to "have", leaves the main place of the essential to another value. To hold health as the essential is a manner of pragmatically limiting one's horizon to the tangible: everything goes on apparently as if, in the optic of certain informants, the majority of young people, the realization of the self limited itself to the quality of the body, to health, without concern to an opening to other values provided by societies in the course of time and whose oldest members were the stronger supporters.

10. Being or Having Among Those in Good Health

It is equally symptomatic that the analogy of wealth is more utilized among superior classes than that of being, whereas manual workers take an opposed attitude: those workers however, in speaking of medicine, speak significantly more of money (cf. our studies 1975 a and b). Would then health be more *wealth* for those who are richer and would it be less for those who are poorer? One would be tempted to admit it if one took into consideration only the two extreme partners of the social scale in the industrialized areas. But this is less visible when one has observed that those who are the most insistent on this theme are often not the best remunerated members of society: employees and those in agriculture. Is it necessary to differentiate? Are not those who most expect an increase in their incomes more inclined to compare health to wealth?

The other formula comes back to holding health for *the essential*. the same preponderance among agricultural workers, then employees over the middle classes and even more over higher classes. For the ones and for the others this means that, with health, the other realities of personal, familial and professional life are safeguarded, saved: health brings them all, it is their pre-condition. Inversely, if health is compromised, personal and family resources appear threatened, professional or occupational projects appear somehow mortgaged. And even if a third party intervenes to partially pay or compensate for treatment and lost salaries, it is certain that such payments or compensations still leave a heavy burden upon those whose incomes are quite modest: in fact, resources available from sickness insurances would not be sufficient to install oneself in sickness, so that, for most people of modest revenues, the loss of health often has nefarious, sometimes catastrophic consequences. And, on the contrary, the maintenance of health means safeguarding the rest: thus it is the primary role of health which makes it literally the essential.

Whether it be either *the essential* or *the greatest wealth,* health thus verifies the already mentioned etymology (Ch 1) of the Latin verb *valere:* to feel well, to be in good health. It is the **fundamental value**, that without which the others loses their value but through which they have value. It is at the same time *salvation*, in the precise measure that the future of individuals and those of families depend on it. As long as there is health, there is survival: there remains, in some fashion, hope concerning the time to come. It is precisely in this respect that a certain continuity exists between these two definitions placing health as a *value* and those we have regrouped under the term of *vitality* and which characterize the middle classes.

11. Recapitulation

After having moved, in the preceding chapters, from lived health to perceived health, we have pursued here the concept of *perceived* health to that of *represented* health, starting from another part of the verbal materials obtained in our two investigations by open-ended and close-ended questions.

Just as in the themes of prevention, of hygiene, of equilibrium and of vitality, one can see in those of non-sickness, in those of psychological well-being, in those of the hedonistic usage of life, in those of the value of health, that more critical level where the respondents locate themselves to perceive health through realizations of which they have the initiative and in which they feel themselves in better position to seek it for itself.

Nevertheless, these three last notions represent, in comparison with the three previous ones, a stage of a more advanced **personal appropriation of health:** that one is then perceived not any more at the service of society, but more in function of the developmental strategies of the self. The *ego* itself constitutes, little by little, a center of interest in competition with that of society.

Thanks to that emergence of the individual *ego*, a new meaning is conferred on health, thus promoted to the rank of a *value*, that one without which other social and personal realities lose theirs, but through which they acquire a value. Already, in the previous group of themes, vitality had introduced the notion of the will to live of individuals as a personalized finality: here we are dealing with the social finality of health as value.

Health even becomes the object of a complex social representation: its ascent in the most important and demanding preoccupations of recent times is of concern as much to economists, as political scientists, and sociologists as it is to health professionals. And that explains in what sense we have wandered from perceived to represented health. Thus is the new perspective in which the image of health reveals itself as a carrier of certain characteristics of the image of the self: this will be the object of our next chapter.

Chapter 9

From the Image of Health
to that of the Self

1. The Language of the Respondents

In our research work (Ch3 to 8), when we examined the speech of the informants as it presented itself, one could avoid asking oneself again the more general question (cf the end of chapter 3) of their **linguistic capacity**: observed verbal behaviors, notably in the open-ended questions, call upon the usual lexical categories used in the domains treated in the questionnaire. But, of course, one asks oneself about the comprehension that the various respondents have of the terms in the posed questions and the signification of those they use in their answers.

Concretely this is a double question (cf ch 3). Does an **identical expression** have the same meaning for all? Inversely, do different expressions contain different notions? Let us examine, in the health sector, two questions, that we have analyzed.

Is the notion of *prevention* the same among higher classes and manual workers ? In one of our studies (1975), we brought out a diversity of emphases on the subject of prevention according to the context of our research. Here our questioning is more radical: does prevention among those in agriculture (they are the ones who insist most on this) have the same signification among the middle classes or cadres (those who insist the least)? Or even, among urban workers themselves, does the prevention of rural workers have the same signification as that of urban workers? According to our two previous chapters, the city dwellers (workers and also employees) are the only ones to speak of *living as long as possible;* they cite more often the adage *better to prevent than to cure;* they find themselves with agricultural workers in *to watch oneself;* then the workers and those in agriculture agree with higher classes on *to know oneself well,* but they dissociate themselves from them in *having a regular check-up*. To these unequal emphases, one should add the connotation of the same expressions in current life or in the occupational activities of some and others.

The example of *equilibrium* is clearer, since the distinction between the physical and the mental is used more by higher classes than by manual workers, employees locating themselves in the middle and resorting more to the global expression of *good equilibrium*. By contrast, the fact that those in agriculture predominate not only in comparison with higher classes, but also over workers when it is a question of *equilibrium in the family*, can be explained by the importance of family solidarity in an agricultural enterprise.

Inversely, do not **different words** have the same meaning for different social strata? Thus the *equilibrium* of higher classes is not necessarily very far from the *hygiene* of the workers and of employees or of the *prevention* of those in agriculture and of workers. The *good morale* of workers rejoins perhaps the *good humor*, the *happiness* and the *joy of living* of employees or *life without constraint* of higher classes. Similarly, *physical aptitudes* among manual workers is perhaps but another modality of the *reference to the body*, dear to the higher classes.

The problem of the linguistic capacity that we have just raised could however only be resolved in the framework of complementary research to be undertaken logically in the future.

2. The Socio-Cultural Situations of the Respondents

Without doubt, health is also the recipient of varying meanings from one group to the other, in the measure to which it does not play the same role among all and to which it is not the object of the same expectations. Many reasons can be found for this.

a. Let us first note the progressive transition **from civilizations of penury**, where epidemics sharply posed the problem of survival, both in the sense of the here and there as well as the beyond, **to civilizations of abundance,** where consumer goods constitute the most dangerous threat to the increase in the life expectancy. In these latter civilizations, one can take the time to think about one's health: one thus accedes to the wish to increase life on earth, the only one in which all still believe.

The advertising which incites consumption enhances health in linking it to personal development, to unfolding, to youth, to beauty. Better nutrition is held to increase physical resistance to illness in spite of the new menaces coming from excesses and from pollution. The idea of check-ups tends to be universally accepted. Even the advertisements of the pharmaceutical firms emphasize the interest in health, making of this a real object of business, something that can also be found in the publicity for certain types of nutrition, for example products said to be *natural* or mineral waters.

The invitation to a healthy life reinforces the need of so-called *sanitary* installations, resort to water for personal care and for baths, the search for relaxation and leisure. Mass media attract public attention to medical discoveries, to surgical exploits, to the new varieties of flu, to medical research. The tradition of physicians or scientists who become writers adds to its impact: after Carrel and Lecompte du Nouy, today it is Jean Bernard and Jean Hamburger, Jacques Monod and François Jacob, etc...

b. The transition **from the countryside to the city** [a], makes people more interested or concerned with their health. In the city one fears illnesses more and particularly death. The cemetery, often located in the center of the village near the church, is relegated or rejected to the periphery of urban agglomerations. Girls, at an earlier time, at the age when they still did not know how babies were born, had already learned about death (of an aged relative, of a neighbor, etc); those of today who are exposed to sexual education in the school, do not see death so closely. The constraints of urban life make it so that many people die alone or in the company of people of their age in a nursing home or in an hospice. Thus in the measure to which the taboos on sex disappear, taboos on death are strengthened. The more representations of health are emphasized, publicized, the more those of death are attenuated, discreetly put aside, even hidden.

c. This may explain that one passes, little by little, **from the negative to the positive aspects of health**, the former predominating in the civilizations of penury and in rural regions. In moving to abundance and to the city, people seem to insist less on the curative and more on the preventive [b], less on the somatic and more on the psychic.

Taken less as a hereditary "given" or as a personal characteristic, health would be more easily envisaged as dependent on life habits and as a fruit of a pedagogical processes and of an educational action, at any rate as the value without which all other

---

[a] On the Latin opposition *urbs-rus*, see Maget (1968), page 1253. The entire text of this author should be read as a more general framework to our chapter 9 or even to our entire book.

[b] This explains why aspirations for prevention are precisely more intense among those in the rural areas who do not benefit from it yet, whereas city dwellers take it for granted.

aspects are not, any more, the same, whether it is a question of work, of sport, of happiness or of the hedonistic use of life.

In this new perspective *pain* itself seen in the past as the expression of a sanction or of an unhappy fate, or a condition for salvation, takes the meaning of a necessary signal in most afflictions: and precisely illnesses that are not accompanied by such a beneficial warning are seen as more to be feared, since they reveal themselves too late for the application of an efficacious remedy. And, moreover, with the discovery of anesthetics, in particular novocain (in 1932), pain becomes controllable and thus appears more tied to physical-chemical conditions and less tied to the sphere of the sacred.

d. According to another perspective, health is not any more considered solely as an objective reality, depending on more and more general conditions (demographic factors, standards of living, environment) and leading to shocking disparities, but it is also lived and felt in the intimate life of everyone. As a **subjective reality**, health certainly seems variable from one cultural era to another, from one socio-occupational milieu to another, but it becomes more and more demanded as a *right* that society must provide in conformity with the technological possibilities of the moment. Illness or morbidity takes the signification of a social scourge of a probabilistic nature: it is a risk that weighs on the collectivity, a risk that affects unfairly some of its members and which other members must, in a solidary fashion, accept to finance or cover.

e. It is as a personal reality, a claim against society, that health is seen through Rousseau-like tendencies of a **return to nature**. Nature is held to be free of all illness or as a restorer of the damages inflicted by life in society (*natura medicatrix*). This idyllic conception of health, coming from a benevolent nature is more or less validly exploited by magazines and movements in favor of more natural conditions of human existence.

f. In this last case as in the previous one, health is felt more or less vaguely as a **fundamental need** or an essential desire. Usually, the consciousness of the need for health develops or grows with medical and pharmaceutical consumption, and with the consumption of other economic goods (food, paid vacations, etc), in such a way that the neediest in the economic sense seem to be the least demanding in the domain of health. One then conceives of all the difficulties there are to harmonize the disparate objective and subjective realities of health.

g. One is equally struck by another contrast: on one hand, the ease with which our informants make, without being aware of it, of their image of health a kind of mirror of their social position; on the other, the difficulty with which, by contrast, they look upon that health as depending from an **active commitment** on their part. In other words, they perceive it as depending little on training, on exercise. Individuals who are in the best of health are at the same time the most "performing": just like life, of which it is an expression, health is maintained through a certain struggle, in renewed efforts. In this respect, the statement *to do nothing is to conserve it* (cf § 3, chapter 9) would only be valid for those categories of manual workers exhausted by overwork, particular their tasks. Precisely, in societies where work activities are more and more taken over by mechanization and automation, it is vital that sport take over from work or complement it adequately.

3. Health as a Value

a. No less striking is another observation on the totality of definitions of health, whose evident function as a mirror of the individual and of his milieu we have frequently noted: one can, more deeply though less easily, detect in it a reflection of the **meaning that each human being gives to his life.** The sense of life reveals itself in the manner in which each one locates himself in relation to the *one* (in French *on*) and to the *"I"*, to *uti* and to *frui*, to *otium* and *negotium*. It is transparent when health is held either as wealth (i.e., to have, to possess), or as the essential (to be). In order for that meaning to be fully revealed, one would need to explicitly question the same informants with a brand new question. In sum, it would come to ask them if, for them, health is the sun which illuminates their lives from dawn to dusk. In the Indo-European language, the notion itself of *god* derives from the luminous, the celestial in opposition to the human which is terrestrial [c].

b. With the meaning of life, one rejoins health not only as an eminently individualized value in the unique destiny of each one, but at the same time as a **universal value** at the level of all mankind. To recognize its universality while at the same time to free it from all economic and cultural constraints, is it not to confer to health a **transcultural value** ? Initially, associated to religious salvation, propagated by salutations and by the institutions tied to illness and medicine (cf chs.1 and 2), health is less and less relegated in its negative representations and sought more and more for itself. Up to the present, everything went on as if human beings did not dare look at it

---

[c]   See Benveniste (1969), tome II, page 180.

directly. As in the Platonic myth of the cavern (Republic VII), as long as human beings are chained, their back turned toward light, they see only the shadows of the realities of health and understand discourses on health only as a function of these shadows. If one releases prisoners, most of them still seek to go back to their prison, going sometimes as far as to curse those who want to liberate them. But for those who accept a movement of conversion and go back to the origins of the light, there is a true and durable emancipation through access to reality itself. This is then the sense in which health, more and more, is on the way of imposing itself in its positive aspects.

4. Health as a Mirror of Socio-Economic Positions

At the socio-economic level, the essential diversities in defining health appear as a function of whether one is a manual worker or a member of the higher managerial classes : whence the **bipolar** interpretation. The same distribution lends itself to a **three-fold** interpretation, according to which, between managers and rural manual workers, employees in certain groupings are associated with workers: a kind of category of citizens, by opposition to those in the countryside. In reality, the two interpretations, far from excluding each other, complement or complete each other: in the three-fold structure, indeed, the bipolarity "cadre-manual" remains, the intermediary element constituting then more a stage of transition from one pole to another than a sort of third pole in a triangular position.

Such a duality of structure illustrates well the function of interpretation in the work of the investigator formulating hypotheses that are confirmed or disconfirmed by the confrontation with the empirical reality. The bipolar interpretation is that much more meaningful as it is systematic: its irreducible part is justified and clearly remains in certain perspectives that cannot be reduced to a three-fold structure, however more satisfying it is for other perspectives. For, certainly, the closer one is to empirical classifications, the less there is meaning; but the more one resorts to abstract classifications, the more the meanings become clear. Thus, to characterize the socio-occupational tendencies, we had to resort to dyads or triads of notions. Let us recall the two examples:

First of all, taken from the Latin, the **dyad** of the *uti* and of the *frui* appears typically bipolar. One can verify it when *the full form* or the *work* among manual workers, oppose *the reference to the body* among the managers. Why should we not see there different uses of the body (Boltanski, 1971)? In the first case, the body is related to two physical aptitudes: work and sport. In the second case, it is a question of *not feeling one's body* or *to feel well in one's skin*: i.e. the body is brought back to the well-being it procures or the not feeling well which it does not cause. According to that bipolar perspective, the *uti* is on the side of the manual workers; the *frui* is with the higher classes. However, if one takes up these four definitions by age, the bipolarity brought about by the *uti-frui* dyad is not sufficient to express a greater complexity. Thus, *not to feel one's body* has a U-shaped distribution; *to feel well in one's skin* has a bell-shape distribution; *the full form* characterizes the youngest ones ; *work*, the oldest. In that circumstance, the *uti* is manifestly on the side of work, whereas by opposition to that one, the full form receives from *frui* its full signification. Let us say that in the measure that it represents sports activities in opposition to activities typically useful for work, the full form has to be then attached to the category of objectives external to the individual: it is to be attached to the category of *frui*. There is then an apparent paradox in characterizing the full form sometimes as *frui* when one opposes it, according to age, to work, or sometimes as *uti* when, with work and by opposition to the reference to the body, it differentiates agricultural workers from higher classes or managers. It is therefore possible to think that it does not fulfill exactly the same function when it distinguishes agricultural workers from managers. Or to conclude that the dyad *uti-frui* does not succeed in reducing to the binary schema the reality, somewhat richer or more complex, of the observed mentalities

The second example has to do with the opposition of the *one* (in French, *on*) and of the *"I"*. Following this study, it is plausible to locate references to the value of health (*the essential, the greatest wealth*) on the side of the *one*; then the references to the self (*not to feel one's body*) on the side of the *"I"*. Here also the opposition comes from a certain systematisation that brings about the meaning: the *one* is certainly predominant among manual workers while also being present among managers: the *"I"* predominates among managers, while manifesting itself also among manual workers. This is why a series of groupings of definitions is undeniably centered on the *"I"*, on personal norms and on a certain preponderance of introversion, whereas another series of groupings is centered on *one*, on social norms and a certain preponderance on extroversion (cf ch. 3, Table IV). Everything takes place then as if the position of the manual workers in the social hierarchy did not facilitate the expansion of their individual personality, but on the contrary facilitated their integration with anonymous social functions, whereas that of managers brought them more mastery of themselves and of others, more of a critical distance vis-a-vis abstract values and concrete objectives of society.

In sum, those who preside and supervise others in executing collective tasks express, in their representations of health, **more**

emancipation. And those who are assigned to these collective tasks manifest in their manner to see health **more dependence.** One then comes upon one of the deepest significations of the socio-occupational distribution of definitions of health: individuals see in their image of health a reflection of their own selves. Health has the function of serving as a mirror of individual social positions in the system of collective production, itself dominated in our industrial societies by the fundamental duality of manual workers (whether city-dwellers or in the countryside) and cadres, managers, higher classes.

Consequently, whether utilized as object or enjoyment, health becomes equally the stake in the confrontation of individuals in social competition: those have a representation of health as a function of their position of dependence or emancipation. Just like work and culture, health is more or less personalized as a function of the role each one has in society at large.

5. Image of the Self and Image of Health

We could pursue this analysis with themes that are certainly less predominant among our informants, but no less interesting. We prefer however to stick to the previous elements of our enumeration and to review our analysis of health in proposing a more general hypothesis in order to interpret the totality of the obtained definitions of health. And to put forward that idea, already expressed (cf. chapter 8), according to which, finally, the *image* of health among our informants would be a sort of a replica of their image of themselves: in sum, an *image of the self;* reflected in the mirror of health.

Indeed, in certain respects, health is also, in man, the reflection of his environment, as we developed this theme earlier (1977a). But the human individual finally perceives what surrounds him through what he is and what he lives: in other words, he has a representation corresponding to the affections of his sensitivity (in the Cartesian sense of the words). Nevertheless, this human being, so well equipped to seize what surrounds him and is useful to him, how can he **apprehend in himself his health?** Neither object of external perception, nor, properly speaking, object of introspection, health escapes his grasp, justifying thus the embarrassment, so often noted, of which it is the occasion: one can then understand that most defined it in the negative or in reference to illness and medicine, where it is guessed as through a transparency, a watermark.

And from the moment when man seeks to define health in its reality in himself, he inevitably comes to characterize it through what he discovers in himself: his needs, his desires, his projects, his illusions sometimes and even his disillusions. This is why the **more** positive definitions of health send us back an image so clear of the deep will of the *ego:* to realize himself fully beyond society. At least it is a process more frequent among higher classes, who are freer from benefitting the constraints of social life and benefiting more from the resources of a society whose essential components they control.

Among manual workers, the *ego* will be less the carrier of expansionist individual aspirations and more affected by the realizations and the projects of society for which their health is more the instrument than the finality. Partially alienated from himself, the modern needy worker tends more to satisfy his fundamental needs than to procure for himself care in the order of the superfluous: his health has no justification other than in the pursuit of the necessary, that is imposed by society as well as by himself. To define health only through hygiene and prevention, through non-illness or good morale, is to claim **a health that is prisoner of the constraints and the servitudes of life in society.** But it is, by this fact itself, to express oneself in that radical dependence.

There is, indeed, equally among manual workers the constellation of attitudes that are happiness, joy of living, good humor. In such a perspective, the *dream* offers the manual worker, whose body is alienated by work, the possibility to recoup the psychic part of his being, the one that is nourished by the images of films and magazines: and from that moment on, health appears less a physical entity than the **interior melody** that one sings for oneself in that personal domain that is the dream. And now, one perceives better the originality of that sort of Third World of health when one compares it to the world of the higher classes, centered on their body, and their skin, which they have conserved or reconquered from the encroachments of social life and which marks the center of gravity of their emancipation, as the keystone of the freedom they won.

Fundamentally, to recognize in the reality of health an image of the self for each one is still a way to hold, following the Greeks of the past, man as the **microcosm** or the reduced model of the macrocosm such, at least, that be believes he perceives. In this sense, health has the value of the essential: it is part of the essence of man in his relationship to the world. Or it has the value of the greatest wealth: through it one accedes to having all the rest in the sense, according to the current proverb, that "there is no wealth but health".

6. Recapitulation

When they speak of health, respondents resort to a language that has a double meaning: the same formulation may have diverse contents and different words, in certain cases, mean the same.

Beyond the language, the socio-cultural situations of our informants are also an issue. For example, the fact of a transition from a rural civilization where goods are scarce to that of an urban civilization of plenty. Health emerges from that phenomenon transformed little by little: it is better perceived in its positive, subjective, ecological aspects, as a need and a commitment, giving meaning to life, carrier of a universal, even transcultural, value.

Such transformations, so radical, are accompanied by a differentiation of the representation of health as a function of the recent stratification of industrialized societies and the competition of individuals in their search for incomes and culture, to which health is added as a new stake.

Many of the elements of the previous analyses converge then toward an image of health intervening as a reflection of the image of the self among the oppositions and the rivalries among individuals and between social strata, of which it has become one of the aces or one of the essential stakes.

Recapitulation of Part III

1. Recalling the Stages of the Analysis

In this Part III, we have chosen to distribute our principal groups of themes on health in three chapters:
- what has to do with the body (ch.6),
- what has to do with prevention, hygiene, equilibrium, vitality (Ch.7),
- what concerns non-sickness, well-being, pleasure, value (Ch.8).

A synthetic chapter seeks to go from the image of health to the image of the self (Ch.9).

2. The Body and Health

Following the unequal insistences of ones and others on the different notions used to speak of health as a function of the body, there appears a clear socio-occupational differentiation of representations referring to physical activities (*work, sport)* or to body sensations *(to feel well in one's body, full form)*. Health reveals itself as being the totality of the qualities making the body capable of fulfilling these internal and external functions and therefore to locate the individual *"I"* as living in the midst of its natural and social environment.

Referring to health thus lived, how do respondents accede to perceived health?

3. Health in Prevention, Hygiene, Equilibrium, Vitality

To refer to attitudes and behaviors of *prevention, hygiene* or to the analogy of *equilibrium*, is to describe health as it is perceived by informants, when they feel they have the initiative of such realizations, unequally sought as a function of their groups (age, sex, socio-occupational category).

4. Health As Non-Sickness, Well-Being, Pleasure, Value

When it is a question of themes evoking *non-illness, psychological well-being, the hedonistic usage of life, value of health* as *the essential* or as *the greatest wealth,* there is an imperceptible passage from perceived to represented health. In the process of this transition, the socio-occupational differentiations of representations of health accentuates themselves, a question which we have touched upon in the course of the previous chapters.

5. From the Image of Health to the Image of the Self

This is why we have attempted to go back from the image of health to the image of the self which can be perceived, more or less, by each respondent. Health itself, reflection of the preoccupations of each one and of each social group through the symbols and the analogies which it elicits, becomes in turn a faithful mirror of what man is and what he has in the midst of his society and of the universe.

Part IV

Health And Society:
Socio-Economic Reflections

INTRODUCTION

The study of cultural images of health according to socio-economic categories, to cultural levels and to age groups in the population having been completed, the next question is that of the functions of health in society.

Such is the object of this fourth part by Professor Mark G. Field (of Boston and Harvard University) in two chapters:

- significance of health in society (ch.10),
- issues and questions: socio-economic and political strategies in health systems (ch.11).

Chapter 10

Significance of Health in Society

1. Social Roles

An examination of health in society and of the importance it occupies must start from the fact that any society or group or family depends for its existence on the performance by its members of a series of social roles. These roles and their performance are not simply the result of an arbitrary or capricious definition either by society or the individual: they represent tasks and important duties, often indispensable or necessary for the survival of groups and the individual. There is therefore an obligatory, normative and often coercive element in the concept of the social role. One neglects it only at one's risk and peril. Such neglect, in fact, constitutes social deviance to which we shall return.

From a theoretical viewpoint, one could go as far as to define *any group or society as consisting of a structure of roles* that exist independently of the individuals who fill them. That structure, which has developed in the course of time, pre-exists the individual social actor and persists after that specific actor has gone and been replaced by a new one.

Let us take, for example, the maternal role. There is, it is true, an absolute biological link between the *mother* and *child* which, one might think, automatically and *naturally* defines what the mother's obligations are toward her child, what some would call maternal instinct. But, at the time the umbilical cord is cut and with the exception of nursing, that relationship between mother and child becomes a social relationship in which it is the society and the culture which define, to a large extent, the contents of that role. That role includes certain responsibilities and privileges that are socially and culturally sanctioned and often enforced. This is independent of the affective ties that may or, as the case may be, not exist between mother and child.

Eventually, the role of the child, as it grows up, is also defined by society, and, just like all social roles, it becomes complementary to that of the mother. Thus the child also has certain responsibilities and privileges that derive from that definition of roles, again independently of emotional or other psychological ties.

At the same time one should not consider the concept of social role as something static or unchanging. With its theatrical origins (the script), the idea of role includes the possibility and the reality of *interpretation*, and re-interpretation. Every mother takes care of her child, and fulfills her maternal role obligations in her own particular way. Every president of the United States brings to the presidency (which is a social role) his own idea on how to fulfill his mandate And that interpretation becomes the departure point for his successor.

Another highly visible example, nowadays is the evolution of the *role of women* in contemporary industrial society. Another consists changing family roles: traditionally the role (and the obligation) of the child was to take care of his or her parents when they became old or infirm. In modern life, that personal obligation has become attenuated. It is often society (at least industrial and modern society), with its system of social security and social welfare, that has assumed the obligation to take care of the elderly (parents) and the child is relieved to a greater or smaller extent of the direct duty of care and support. On the other hand, that child often pays taxes, partly destined to the support of elderly persons.

As mentioned above, the roles of mother (or parent) and of the child depend originally from the biological relationship, but not necessarily. That relationship is a structured point of departure at the intersection of the biological and the social. The existence of adoptive or of foster parents, or even wet nurses, shows that the roles of mothers (and of course fathers) can be played even in the complete absence of any biological links: these role prescriptions are sociological and describe the contents of socially expected types of behavior. The existence of a structure of social roles in any society or group is indispensable for the functioning of such groups or of society. These roles can be grouped into different sectors (the family, the economy, the polity, etc) which facilitate and permit the survival of the social system. They provide an element of stability through the predictability of role performance.

We have mentioned prominently the role of the mother and of parents. This is part of the family institutions, institutions of capital importance, for example, in assuring the protection of the child from birth on (and of course even before birth). Without such provisions, the child could remain without care or protection (and might soon die) and without the initial socialization, which is paramount for the formation of personality and for the transmission of culture from one generation to the other. *Culture* is here taken in the sense of *the non-genetic inheritance of mankind.* It is what man creates, shares and passes from one generation to another, such as language, ideas, customs, knowledge, and, as we have seen, role definitions. The family, as a social institution, in addition to its protective and socialising functions, regulates sexual access (by defining who are acceptable sexual partners and who are not) and provides an element of stability in society. There is strong reason to believe, for example, that the incest taboo is not the result of some perception of the negative genetic effects of incestual relationships, but rather of the destructive results that such relationships would have on family stability, and indeed its very existence as a group of persons solidary to each other.

The role of the worker is critical for the functioning of the system of industrial production, as well as the role of the farmer or peasant for the production of the food indispensable to maintain both the agricultural and the urban work forces and others (children, housewives, students, the elderly i.e; those not engaged in the economic system).

Political institutions define also the roles of those who must take decisions that affect groups in the society, or the society as a whole (including its relationship with other societies), as well as the use of *force to maintain civil order* or peace. This is why, as we have insisted, social institutions are endowed with a certain moral value, and are sometimes embodied in the legal order: these institutions impose obligations to members of society in the different roles they are called upon to play. Non-performance, according to expectations, creates generally the problem of social deviance, a major threat to the social order and to the probabilistic aspect of social role performance. Illness or trauma pose in this respect, an important question to society and the individual.

2. The Social Impact of Illness

It is self evident that society depends on the social control over the actions of its members: this control assures the functioning of society and role performance according to expectations, particularly those roles that are vital to life and the survival of the social system. This derives from the fact that *human action* or *comportment is not genetically programmed,* it is in no way automatic or *natural,* for the individual has the latitude to do what he wants, to act in his or her own fashion. This is why, as we have insisted all along, social institutions mold or shape the actions of individuals in the support of the social system.

One major problem concerns *social deviance,* which we already mentioned, i.e., non-conformity with moral, social or legal norms. The failure on the part of members of society concerning their social role expectations (for example a mother who abandons, neglects, or mistreats her child) becomes almost immediately an important question. We are speaking here of a willful failure on the part of the actor, and thus subject to some kind of social retribution such as punishment, blame, ostracism, legal action, and so forth. The failure to perform certain roles, for example the concerted withholding of economic role performance as in the case of a strike, also shows the political power that role performance (or non-performance) can exert.

There is however another series of problems that affect the performance of roles: these are the problems due to involuntary incapacity (or incapacity judged as such) on the part of individuals to perform as expected. This incapacity immobilizes individuals and makes them partially or totally incapable to perform their role obligations. We are speaking here of the consequences of illness or trauma or the ultimate incapacity of death itself. Illness and trauma present two essential characteristics, one that is well-known, the other less well recognized as to its consequences for the social system

The first one concerns the *personal, subjective, individual aspects of illness, trauma and pain*. This is at the origin of the clinical and therapeutic enterprise. Illness (in its general sense of "bad health") is part and parcel of the human condition: it derives from the physiological characteristics of the organism and of the mental or psychological traits of the personality. It is therefore a universal condition which no human being can escape. This problem exists from the appearance of man and will, no doubt, continue in the future. Physicians, therapists, theologians and philosophers have pondered on its origins and its etiology (is it the work of the devil, a punishment from the gods, or God, the resultant of a poorly balanced style of life or the *sequelae* of a bacteriological or viral invasion); and those who have dealt with the problem through the ages have elaborated different modalities to face these morbid states (prayer, ritualistic acts, contrition, sacrifices, or the injection of an anti-biotic). It is also important to note that most illnesses heal by themselves, automatically if one can use that term, in the light of the mechanisms of self-defense or the immunity that are built in the organism, and without which mankind would not have survived until today. In one sense, the therapeutic or clinical enterprise aims at supplementing and complementing the healing capacity of the organism or of the mind.

The second characteristic derives from the first one: *illness, as well as trauma, may incapacitate members of society from performing their expected social roles and obligations.* Let us return, for a moment, to the mother and her role toward her infant or child. A mother who is seriously ill or febrile or handicapped by a wound or dying cannot, in spite of her best intentions, take care of her child. If there is no one who could replace her, the consequence is that the child may or will die. It is therefore a problem that goes well beyond the personal and subjective aspects mentioned earlier: it is a question of a situation that can become serious for society or for any other grouping, which depend on the performance of all or most of its members in matters of services or products. Let us think, for a moment, of the hundreds, of the thousands of persons on whom we depend in our daily life: those who raise the food we eat, those who transport it from the warehouses to the retail stores, those who drive the buses, the subways, or the trains, those who perform their humble functions in the factories, in the banks, in the restaurants, etc. What would be the consequences if a considerable proportion of those were immobilized by illness ? How many battles and how many wars were lost because a large proportion of the troops were paralyzed by illness or by an epidemic?

In other words, the incapacity that is caused by illness or trauma, poses before society, the very question of its functioning: it is necessary to find a replacement (which is often far from easy), or to face the possibility that certain functions will not be accomplished or certain roles will not be performed.

Of course the impact of illness on society depends on several quantitative and qualitative factors. First of all, it is necessary to have some notion of the number or the proportion of those persons affected by illness: there is a difference between an epidemic and a few cases among the population. In general, industrial firms know what proportion of their workers or employees are likely to be sick; they gear themselves to have available replacements. The same is generally true of schools which have, at their disposal, teachers who may be called at a moment's notice to take over classes. Then it is also important to have a notion of the importance of roles and of the difficulty or the ease to find replacements: one can replace, either temporarily or permanently, a sick mother without perhaps too many difficulties; but a chief of state, a scientist, a person with rare and high qualifications are not so easily replaceable: sometimes they simply cannot be replaced at all. It is also important to take into account the degree of incapacitation of the individual (total, partial), the duration of the incapacity (temporary, long term, permanent, etc), the nature of the cause of that incapacitation. For example, in the distant past, chiefs of state had to show physical power and considerable energy. What is often more important in the contemporary society is not so much physical stamina as mental health and personality organization: we have seen a President of the United States who was a paraplegic and who nonetheless exercised his power and performed his presidential role without being, in that respect, handicapped.

In summary, sickness (in the general sense of the term) has two important consequences that are related to each other. The first one is the impact of sickness on the individual: a personal and subjective impact, including that of pain. The second is the consequence of illness on the individual's capacity to face his or her social role obligations, a consequence that, under certain circumstances, may have grave repercussions, or even catastrophic ones. We may call the first series of events *expressive*, the second *instrumental* or *functional*. The center of gravity of the expressive impact tends to be rather ego-centric. The instrumental or functional impact tends to be more socio-centric since it links the individual to his social role obligations whatever they may be.

The incapacity caused by sickness can be subsumed into five major categories that threaten man regularly: death, illness, handicap, suffering and dissatisfaction.

3. The Health System as a Social Response to Illness

The five conditions given above constitute the goals or better the targets of the health system and of the therapist. We must at the same time recognize again the fact that these conditions mobilize, in man, *systems of self-defense*, whether it be immunity or the various automatic mechanisms that protect the organism (blood coagulation in contact with air, for example, or the various psychological defense mechanisms that protect the integrity of the individual, his personality, his *ego*: for example repression, sublimation, displacement, and so on). Being more or less built-in and automatic, these mechanisms are not the objects of the conscious control of the individual. The *vis medicatrix naturae* is what has permitted the human and animal races to survive.

In the measure to which man has judged that these automatic defense mechanisms were not sufficient to face the threats posed by illness and premature mortality, he has, in the course of the centuries, developed his own conceptions of the etiology of sickness, of its causes and antecedents, and of the manner in which to reduce its impact. These conceptions depend, to a large extent, of *the idea that man has of health*. Such images of health are linked to the general conception of the place of man in nature and in society. It is the positivistic approach of science which, in the present societal context, determines, to a large extent, the way in which man sees the factors that affect his health. Scientific medicine dominates and monopolizes actions toward illness. It however should be pointed out that this view of the origins of illness is historically quite recent; that, in the course of centuries, illness was seen in quite a different optic, often religious or mystical; and that the nature of remedial measures was a function of such conceptions. *And even in the modern health care system, science and positivism cannot meaningfully explain to man certain aspects of suffering or of death.* For example, the death of an elderly person may be a sad event, but not totally unexpected and not going beyond the ordinary, given the fact that life is limited. The death of a soldier on the field of battle is a tragedy, but it can be explained or rationalized: he died defending the motherland or for a cause. On the other hand, there are deaths that make no sense at all: a person in full bloom, a young person hit by a drunken driver, for example. At the scientific level, medically, biologically, physiologically, an explanation can be given: concussion, shock, hemorrhage, etc. But such an explanation cannot be satisfactory at the emotional level; it does not answer the question *why* ? It is a different level of explanation that is invoked: often, as we mentioned it, it is religion that provides an explanation of sorts, like the ritual phrase that "the Lord giveth and the Lord taketh away, blessed be the name of the Lord".

Scientific medicine, using its own optic, disposes of certain modalities to face problems of ill-health and trauma. We can distinguish at least six of them:

- prevention,
- diagnosis and prognosis,
- treatment,
- rehabilitation,
- custodial care (take care of sick person for whom nothing medically can be done),
- health education.

These modalities are cultural entities: these are ideas, concepts, prescriptions, recipes, methods that health personnel employ to deal with the above-mentioned problems. But this cultural analysis of the health system would not be complete, if one did not also examine the sociological aspect, i.e. the manner in which health personnel fulfill their different roles (Fabrega, 1976), as well as the organization of such personnel, their legal position and other aspects of their occupational positions. In general, one can say that those who work full-time in the health system resort to the scientific approach of the six modalities enumerated above to face the problems posed by morbid states. The activities of health personnel may be defined as the Gross Medical or Health Product of the Health System. It consists in all the activities that the *personnel pursue in the course of a specific time period* (let us say one year) in their efforts to limit or reduce the impact of illness on the individual and society (Field, 1974).

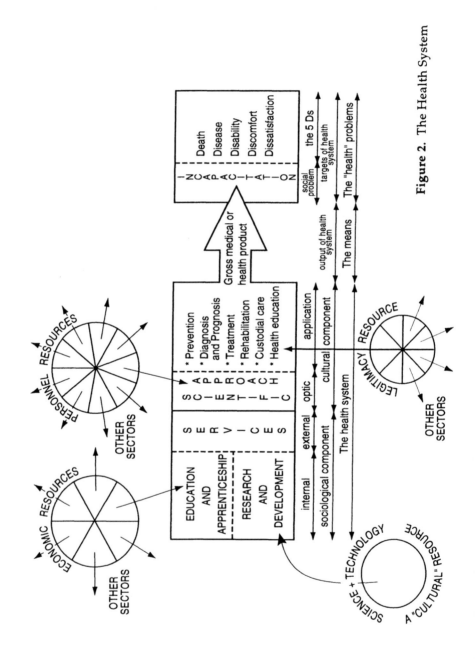

Figure 2. The Health System

The health system such as it is described in Figure 2, and particularly its sociological elements, can be divided into three components: one external, and two internal.

By the external component we designate the services or the outputs produced by the system in direct response to the five problems posed by threats to health. It is, in fact, *what the health system brings to society:* its *raison d'être*, its function, its mandate, its mission. It is for such services that one consults a physician, that one is admitted into a hospital or a clinic. It is the final product of the health system. However that system could not function, nor could it deliver its Gross Medical or Health Product, without the contribution of the two internal components.

The first one consists sociologically in arrangements that permit the health system to reproduce itself, i.e. to proceed to the replacement of personnel who being human are always growing old and eventually retiring or dying, thus unable to perform their occupational roles. Every year, therefore, a proportion of such personnel "quits" the health system. To replace them, two questions must be resolved. The first is that *of the motivation and the recruitment of replacements,* keeping in mind that there is a variety of other sectors in society that also need replacements ; this therefore creates competition (manifest or latent) as the number of qualified young people is always finite. This recruitment of replacements constitutes but one aspect of the problem: once recruited, these replacements must be educated, trained, formed, socialized to fulfill their future roles in the health system. Such is *the task or the mission of schools* (of medicine, nurses, technicians, etc). and of different programs of apprenticeship for these students (internships, for example). It should be noted that this process of replacement must take place continually, from year to year. If this process were to be interrupted or seriously slowed down, the consequences for the health system, and eventually for society, might be serious: this would have an impact on the ability of the system to deliver its Gross Medical Product. In an extreme case, lack of recruitment and replacement would mean that the health system would grind to a halt and disappear. It would probably be replaced by another system so great is the therapeutic need.

We shall not deal here with the quantitative and qualitative changes that take place in this recruitment process. Nor shall we examine the fact that, in the course of time, new health occupations emerge, resulting often from new technologies that require new specialists or technicians. Nor of the process of specialization in general: a process that is more and more intense, leading to certain consequences we shall examine later on. Neither shall we discuss the question of recruitment, for work in the health system, of individuals who contribute to the functioning of the system, but who do not have a specific medical or para-medical training: for example, those who work in hospitals as secretaries, electricians, drivers, carpenters, cooks. Certainly these people contribute to the fashioning of the Gross Medical Product, but their qualifications are not specific to the health care system: they could just as well work in other sectors of society for example in a hotel or an office building. On the other hand, those who are trained specifically for one or the other aspect of the health system might find it difficult to work in other sectors.

The Second Internal Component concerns medical research. It consists in the discovery as well as in the elaboration and the application of general scientific knowledge and of the available technological level in particular to the problems caused by illness and trauma. This application depends, to a large extent, on the scientific and technical sophistication available in the world at large. As this knowledge and technology evolve very rapidly, so does medical knowledge and its applications.

It should also be noted, before proceeding further, that *changes and progress in science and in technology are, of course, not limited to the medical or clinical worlds:* they have an impact on all the domains or sectors of society; they are implicated in almost all fields of activities where they are susceptible to have an effect. Thus scientific and technological developments have a direct impact on agricultural and industrial production ; they modify the system of transportation and communications; and they also have an impact on (and indeed are often generated by) the military sector. Once invented or developed, the internal combustion engine is used by cars, and by planes, by trucks and by ambulances, by tanks and by bombers.

Generally we could say that, of all components of the health system, medical research is the most dynamic, the most revolutionary; it is the component that, in the finally analysis, has radically changed the nature of that system; it is the element that has made it possible to resolve problems that had plagued man for centuries (for example, the prevention of polio). It is also the component that poses new questions, new problems, new dilemmas to society in general. These questions are generally ethical, moral, religious, legal and so on. For example, the ability to prolong life in terminal and irreversible cases poses the question as to who has the right to "turn the machine off". Evidently, scientific progress proceeds at a much faster rate than changes in society, and does lead to what has been called "cultural lag". These problems, caused by scientific and technological advances, cannot be resolved scientifically. For example, questions of ethics or of "meaning" as mentioned earlier. And why this dynamism, these constant and rapid changes that one does not see in other professions and sectors of society (in the legal or in the theological worlds, for example)? It is primarily because scientific research is based on the principle of the discovery of new knowledge, of new relationships or correlations, the elimination of ignorance and superstition and their replacement by verifiable information that is measurable and reproducible.

Research is thus prepared to admit the errors of the past, to change its approaches or theories according to new data, to admit that what yesterday was considered valid and true not necessarily so today or will not be tomorrow. That aspect is thus in marked contrast to the domains, already mentioned, of law and theology: these are areas where tradition and precedent constitute the most important element, where truth and verities have been established once and for all, and where research work often consists in the elaboration and the reinterpretation of what is known, and not to produce or accept revolutionary changes.

The narrow link between the state of knowledge, of science, of technological development and what takes place in the medical world is the result of that second internal component which in fact *translates and applies general scientific discoveries to problems of health and illness*.

It is also important to note that these three components, in the empirical or real world, are very closely linked to each other. A physician, for example, can spend part of his time in clinical activities, in basic or applied research, and in teaching. Such teaching may be directed not only to medical students, but also to colleagues or even the general public (as in health education). To publish in specialized journals is also a form of teaching.

4. What the Health System Receives from Society

The health system, as a specialized sub-system of society, is not in the position to produce or to develop the resources that are necessary to fulfill its mandate. It must receive from the larger society, which it serves, a series of supports that must, in the nature of the case, remain problematic: one cannot assume that these resources will simply and naturally flow into the health system. It is, in fact, a question of a division of labor and of exchanges.

Let us take a more concrete example: a physician who provides care to patients as a full time occupation (whether it be in private practice or as a salaried staff member of a hospital or clinic). What the physician gives his patients is, first, a portion of *time* (a n appointment, a consultation, a surgical intervention). This time, (which is a scarce resource that cannot be stopped, stored or accumulated)

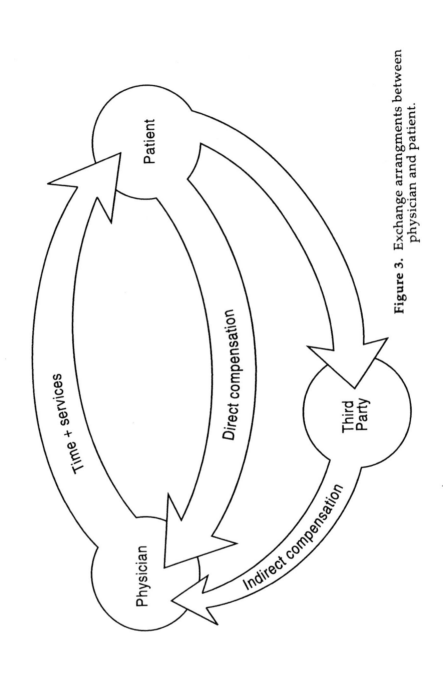

Figure 3. Exchange arrangments between physician and patient.

allows the physician to perform his tasks (diagnostic, clinical, etc). Since he works on a full-time basis, this physician is in no position to take care of his own needs: he cannot raise his own food, make his clothing, educate his children, build his house, etc. This means that his time (i. e. the service he performs) must be compensated by, or exchanged against, the time or times of other individuals who have used it to produce what the medical specialist cannot or does not have the time to produce himself. It is therefore a question of *exchange*. This exchange, in the contemporary world, is usually mediated in monetary terms. It is with these monies that the physician is able, in turn, to purchase what he needs in goods or services. However, it is not indispensable that this exchange take place in monetary terms, though of course it is the most convenient medium of exchange. It could be done in simple barter terms or in providing for the needs of the physician (and his family): the provision of housing, of meals (as for interns, for example) that would permit the physician to take care of his needs.

One could, of course, endlessly quibble or argue on the terms of exchange: are they *fair* ? Is it just that a physician earn much more than a nurse or a worker or someone else? This is a question we shall not tackle here. But what is undisputable is that this exchange must take place, that health and related services be paid, that the loop or circuit be closed. If that system of exchange were to break down, so would the ability of the physician (or any other specialist) to perform his or her occupational roles. A physician who is starved is not in the best position to render services to his patients. Ater the fall of the Soviet Union, and the collapse of its system of socialized medicine, physicians saw their already meager income dwindle even further. Physicians, in some instances, went on strike (or threatened to do so) carrying placards saying, for instance, "A hungry surgeon is dangerous to your health." And even the physician who gives free care, i.e who does not ask for payment from his patients, cannot survive solely through the dewy-eyed gratitudes of his patients. He must be assured of a roof over his head and food on the table.

The health system which we sketched above is symbolically the *physician of society*. It must receive from the society it serves a constant series of resources, not only financial, but also others: at least four. Let us examine them.

A) Economic Resources

We have already discussed this indispensable resource. At the level of the society, it can be expressed as a percentage of Gross National Product or as an average expense per capita or through a whole series of more sophisticated or nuanced metrics depending on the kind of analysis desired. For example, what is the average expense per individual according to age, sex, occupation, location or income. And, then, it is possible to measure what proportion of the GNP is spent for (medical) research, and whether it is basic or applied research. How much for the education of health specialists, and how much is spent for each major diagnostic category.

It is thus possible to calculate, from year to year, what proportion of its total resources each society *decides* to invest into the health sector, as well as other sectors (general education, social security, national defense, industrial investments, etc).

To decide is perhaps too strong a word, for these *decisions* in most instances, are the results of millions of decisions, compromises, of political factors, and conflicts among interest groups. It is only in totalitarian and centralized societies that the government is, more or less, in the position to determine what proportion of the budget and its total resources it will allocate to health and other sectors. But whatever the process, the result (proportion of resources) can be calculated and compared either vertically in terms of historical developments, or horizontally in terms of comparison with other societies. or between regions or areas of the same society. And it should also be noted that, at any one time, the resources available to any social formation are finite. Thus each *decision* to spend or invest into this or that sector must be taken or involves what the economists call *opportunity costs*. To spend in one sector means the inability to spend that money in another one. We shall return to that strategic question of choices.

There are at least, therefore, two levels (in fact many more) concerning these *decisions*. At the national or macroscopic level, the question, already mentioned, is the choice between resources allocated to the health system (or to health in general) and all other sectors of society. But the total amount allocated to health can also be examined at another level to find out or analyse how the health resources themselves are allocated within the health system: how much for education, how much for research, how much for clinical care, how much for prevention, etc? And the analysis can be pushed even further: how much for the different specialties in medicine? How much for basic and applied research? How much for primary health care and how much for secondary or tertiary care ? And in the same vein, what conditions must receive more or less attention and more or less resources. It is in this sense, as E. Berthe has written, that each society chooses its deaths. These analyses can provide a silhouette or profile of health expenditures in general and for each particular sector.

B) Human Resources

The health system must have at its disposal personnel resources that can be defined quantitatively and qualitatively. Quantitatively one may speak of the percentage or *the proportion that health personnel in a country or a specified region constitutes of either the total population, or the working-age population.* This allows us, for example, to calculate if, in the course of time, this percentage (in the same society) remains more or less the same, decreases or increases. The same type of comparison may be made from one society to another. One could then state that society A devotes X percentage of its working-age population to the health system as against Y percent for society B. In general, one can observe that in almost all societies this percentage tends to increase (as does by the way the percentage of the GNP devoted to health). One of the reasons (and only one) comes from the fact that technology used in modern medicine, particularly in hospitals, contrary to what goes in industry, tends to be both labor and capital intensive. In other words, in most instances, technological equipment does not replace human labor but requires, on the contrary, additional personnel to use it, to monitor, calibrate and maintain it. We shall return to this point later on.

From the qualitative viewpoint it is a question to determine health personnel in its many categories. One may divide such personnel into three large classes.

(a) Those who hold a *doctorate,* a higher diploma, like physicians and dentists, etc.

(b) *Those who work in a subordinate or semi-professional position in the health system.* Usually they fulfill the orders of those in category (a), sometimes they work independently. We speak here of nurses, technicians, assistants, etc. One must however note that these personnel have usually received a specialized type of training or apprenticeship, which qualifies them to work in the health system, and not in other sectors.

(c) By contrast, there are those who constitute the *third category:* personnel employed in the health system but *without specific training* for work in that system. We speak, as we have seen earlier, of secretaries, cooks, drivers, etc.

The analysis can be further *refined.* Let's take, first, those who hold a doctorate or the equivalent in category (a). They can be distributed in the large sub-divisions of the health system: medicine, dentistry, pharmacy, university research or industrial research. Then, among them, we can look at physicians, the largest category and the most influential: they can be distributed in several ways. For example, according to the degree of specialization: general medicine, specialized medicine, hyper-specialized medicine, public health, preventive medicine, legal medicine, etc. Then, those in clinical work can be allocated according to their usual place of work: private office, group practice, hospital, out-patient clinic, etc. Or according to their specialty: cardiology, pediatrics, surgery, psychiatry, etc, or; sub-specialties like pediatric surgery or sports medicine. Of course, such classification is not always easy, for often physicians are involved in different areas as we have seen like clinical care, research, teaching, and, increasingly, in administration and management.

A more or less parallel classification may be made for category (b). Thus nurses also tend to specialize according to the different types of patients they handle; others go into administrative positions rather than clinical work.

There is also a certain tendency that is interesting to observe concerning health personnel: the more specialized they become, the more they tend to *delegate* the non-specialized aspect of their work to those who are placed in a subordinate position in the hierarchy. This is the case, for example, of a very busy physician: he can easily ask a nurse to weigh the patient, to take the blood pressure, to withdraw a sample of blood. In her turn, the nurse is tempted to entrust certain domestic or house-keeping tasks (make the beds, for example) to someone who is less qualified (a nursing aid, for example), reserving for herself the specific tasks that demand specialized nursing training. Thus, in the course of time, with specialization, the pyramid of health personnel tends to lengthen in height to the degree that new subordinate positions are created through the process of delegation, or downward transfer of functions; at the same time that pyramid broadens horizontally as the number of specialties increases.

C) Social Legitimacy

The health system also depends on society for its legitimacy as well as political and legal supports.

By *legitimacy;* we mean that what the health system does is considered by the society and its population as important, proper, desirable, and basically honest. As long as this perception persists, the health system and its personnel can work with confidence. But let us imagine a situation where the population would lose trust in the health system: for example, it might be afraid that physicians would harm them or that a sojourn in a hospital represented real dangers, in addition to the condition for which they had been admitted. This is, for example, the thesis of Ivan Illich that health care is dangerous to one's health. Under those conditions the health system would be severely handicapped in carrying out its functions. We must assume that this legitimacy is problematic, and not to be taken for granted as natural or automatic. Legitimacy is conditionally granted by society, and could conceivably be withdrawn under certain conditions.

This brings us to the *political and legal question*: society grants, more or less, a monopoly to so-called scientific medicine, sometimes called allopathic medicine. It restricts and sometimes legally forbids other approaches to health care (homeopathy, treatment by charlatans and quacks and others who are marginal to the officially recognized medical establishment). Again, while this legal and political supports do not appear on first blush as problematic, so much are they considered normal, they are the results of arrangements and specific beliefs that are susceptible of modifications, and challenges. We shall, in the next chapter, return to that question of legitimacy when we examine the challenges and attacks directed at the health system.

D) The Scientific and Technological Resource

Finally, one of the vital resources of the health system is *scientific and technological knowledge*. It is not only an indispensable element as we have already noted, but also a very dynamic one, always in a process of change. The sources of this dynamism are not specific to the health system. They are part of the human patrimony and activates not only medicine but most other sectors of society. The discovery of laser beams has industrial, military and medical applications. One can thus say that medical research is but the elaboration and the application, within the medical domain of general knowledge and technology.

One should also note that this resource is somewhat different from the three previous ones: these resources are always finite and limited, whether it is a question of money, personnel or even legitimacy. Knowledge is a cultural resource : once acquired, it can be used or applied millions of times without diminishing it by one iota: for example, a specific type of procedure or a diagnostic approach. Of course, the discovery of knowledge as well as its application always incur cost.

5. The Comparative Evolution
of Health Systems

Durkheim wrote that comparison is at the heart of the scientific enterprise. One speaks of comparative anatomy or physiology, or comparative political systems (Chase-Dunn, 1979, Elder, 1976). One can also compare health systems in order to have some notion of the characteristics they have *in common as* well as what *distinguishes* them one from another, and also to examine in which direction they seem to be evolving. (Fry, 1969; Litman and Robins, 1971; Mabry, 1971 ; Roemer, 1967; Roemer, 1969). We have already attempted here to define what is the health system. The question is to delineate, with some degree of consistency from one health system to another, what to include and what to exclude. Thus there is no difficulty in including health personnel, as we did earlier, as well as those who work, in a non-professional manner in the health system, for example those who service hospitals. But there are many gray areas: for example is the American *drugstore* part of the health system. The drugstore dispenses prescription items ordered by physicians, but it also sells cigarettes, candy and other sundries. One way to resolve this question is to include, as part of the health system, the dispensation of prescription drugs, and to exclude other activities.

Philosophically, of course, we could say that practically every element in society affects health: housing, income, occupation, roads and means of communications, etc. But this would lead to a conception of the health system as co-terminous with society, thus a *reductio ad absurdum*. But once we have defined, perhaps arbitrarily, the major contours of the health system, we can be reasonably sure that we are comparing similar or comparable entities, and not the traditional apples and oranges.

It seems important, in this respect, to examine the evolution of health systems, and to trace the dynamics of that transformation, i.e to see the elements that contribute to such changes, and to attempt to see in which direction these systems seem to evolve.

We would like to propose two ideas to examine such an evolution of health systems.

A) The Idea of Convergence

A plausible approach to the study of the evolution of health systems is suggested by the *theory of convergence* which appeared after the Second World War. This idea is, in essence, relatively simple. It holds that all around the world a phenomenon is taking place in the economic sphere, with important consequences for the social system and culture. This phenomenon is industralization which creates a new industrial and urban type of society, different in its basic contours from the traditional, agricultural world which it is replacing. Industrialism, fueled by the Scientific and then the Industrial Revolutions holds the promise of abundance resulting from the use of capital equipment to replace human labor and animal sources of energy. This leads to the emergence of social structures dictated by the logic of that type of economic activity. This technological determinism, different from the inexorable historical materialism and teleology of Marx postulates that... "on a number of major dimensions the industrial societies of the world are developing common forms of social organization... differences in institutions, in values, in modes of living, and in the ways individuals relate to each other all become increasingly less marked..., their population more highly educated and increasingly subject to the influence of the media of mass communications... Central is the belief that certain standardized social arrangements have the capacity to shape individual attitudes and behavior in relatively standard ways, even when those arrangements are introduced into quite different cultural contexts". It thus holds that modern industrial societies tend to become increasingly similar to each other (Inkeles and Smith, 1974: Form, 1979).

Among the increasingly common elements, one might note the increasing importance of the time dimension, the use of clocks and watches, the relevance of punctuality and discipline, for example on the assembly line. And those who have stood on street corners in downtown areas of major cities from Paris to Tokyo, from Berlin to New York will recognize certain similarity in the way in which people behave, and even how they dress. And it is not only the logic of industrialism that produces that convergence, but also the principle of emulation and imitation facilitated by instant communication. Industrialism, just like the wheel, need not be reinvented time and again.

The idea of convergence does not mean necessarily that all societies are in the process of becoming like peas in a pod. But rather, it suggests that, in the course of time, the elements in common will become increasingly numerous, and the divergences will become rarer and rarer.

If the theory of convergence has some validity, would it not be applicable to the development of contemporary health systems, since these systems are heavily influenced by universal scientific and technological developments.? In other words, the development of the Means of Medical Production imply that an anti-biotic, a CT scanner or a dialysis machine operate in the same way everywhere, and impose the same logic of utilization. For example the need to maintain strict aseptic conditions in the operation bloc of a hospital requires an organizational structure, a discipline and personality traits that admit of little variation. There are indeed very striking similar characteristics visible in the health systems of industrial society : they consume an ever increasing proportion of the Gross National Product; they become increasingly complex and internally differentiated; they are increasingly bureaucratised and subject to the influence or the pressures, as well as the financing by the State. They experience the constant introduction of medical technology that is both labor and capital intensive, and create problems of integration, increasing costs and the alienation of the patient, to which we shall return.

And yet the theory of the convergence is far from supported by the evidence. A hospital, for example, is part and parcel of the community and the culture in which it is placed. The transition from that community into the hospital is not regulated by pressure chambers and air-tight doors that would insulate the aseptic hospital from its septic surroundings. The hospital is an amalgam of two cultures: the local or societal and the medical; it is a synthesis between two worlds, and therefore hospitals vary from one country to another, or even from one region to the next one.

We chose the *hospital* because it is such a highly visible (and symbolic) embodiment of modern medicine, it is the temple of the religion of applied science and technology to pain, sickness and trauma. It has its analogue in the factory and some patients would say bitterly to the assembly line. It has other analogues where economy of scale and tight organizational requirements dictate structure and behavior (and personality traits): the large supermarket where on can do a week's shopping without exchanging a single word with a human being. And yet, the hospital (or disease palace as the former head of the World Health Organization called it) also symbolizes the encounter between the universal and the particular. Thus we need a more nuanced approach to the question, rather than the simplistic, though attractive one, of convergence

B) A More Nuanced Approach Seems to be More Appropriate.

The health system is the result of a dialectic confrontation and an eventual synthesis between the *universal aspects* of medical science and technology and the *particular elements* visible in each society and culture. Each health system reflects in its organization and its structure this tension between these two elements. Thus a hospital is not only a medical institution that embodies the knowledge and the techniques inherent in the contemporary medical world. The hospital is also part

	Type 1	Type 2	Type 3	Type 4	Type 5
Health System	Emergent	Pluralistic	Insurance/ Social Security	National Health Service	Socialized
General Definition	Health care as an item of personal consumption	Health care as predominantly a consumer good or service	Health care as an insured/ guaranteed consumer good or service	Health care as a state supported consumer good or service	Health care as a state provided public service
Position of the Physician	Solo entrepreneur	Solo entrepreneur and member of variety of groups or organizations	Solo entrepreneur and member of medical organizations	Solo entrepreneur and member of medical organizations	State employee and member of medical organization
Role of Professional Associations	Powerful	Very strong	Strong	Fairly strong	Weak or non-existent
Ownership of Facilities	Private	Private and public	Private and public	Mostly public	Entirely public
Economic Transfers	Direct	Direct and Indirect	Mostly Indirect	Indirect	Entirely Indirect
Role of the Polity	Minimal	Residual Indirect	Central / Indirect	Central / Direct	Total
Prototypes	U.S. ; Western Europe and Russia in xixth Century	U.S. ; Switzerland; South Africa	Sweden; France; Germany; Japan xxth Century; Canada; Italy	Great Britain xxth Century; Australia	Soviet Russia in xxth Century; Eastern Europe; Cuba

Figure 4: A Typology of Health System.

Source : Mark G. Field *"The Comparative Evolution of Health Systems : Convergence, Diversity and Cross-Cultural Issues" in Health and Illness in America and Germany. Edited by Günther Lüschen, William C. Cockerham, Gerhard Kunz, München : R. Oldenbourg Verlag, 1989, pp 15-30.*

and parcel of its community and the national culture in which it exists. And the experience of the World Health Organization in trying to impose, upon developing countries, its own methods of treatment (as the only ones that were scientific and thus correct) has learned that one cannot ignore local and particular cultures. And by the same token, as Lynn Payer has shown, in her book *Culture and Medicine* even clinical practices vary from one country to another. She notes that, "while medicine benefits from a certain amount of scientific output, culture intervenes every step of the way..." For one, doctors in one country rarely read the literature of any country but their own. The American doctor is characterized by his aggressivity, the coronary by-pass operation being performed many times more than in most countries, even those that have the same rates of heart disease. For the American doctor, the heart is just a pump, a machine, an organ fed by tubes that must be unclogged if necessary. For the German doctor, the heart is not just a pump, but an organ with a life of its own that pulsates in response to different stimuli, including emotions, and has metaphoric associations with love and affective feelings. Low blood pressure is considered a problem in Germany, but not to the same degree in England. Lack of appetite is a much more serious symptom for a Frenchman than for an Englishman or a Swede. The hospice movement is well developed in England, because of a greater acceptance of death and dying, whereas Americans regard death as the ultimate failure.

Such differences thus force us to temper our view of convergence. There is a tremendous diversity in health systems around the world, and even in the health systems of highly industrialized societies. This diversity also limits, to some important degree, the transferability of organizational patterns from one society to another, as we shall see below in connection with the Canadian experience and its relevance for the United States. And yet, in spite of these diversities, we can try to tease out a typology of health systems with their main characteristics as seen in Figure 4.

Finally, the comparative examination of health system can proceed along two dimensions or axes, each one not excluding the other (Fry and Farndale, 1972)

a) The first approach is *historical, longitudinal, temporal, evolutionary* or *diachronic*. It follows the development and changes in the health system over time (as well as the evolution of morbidity and mortality) to trace changes and developments that have taken place in society and in the health system, including the introduction of new knowledge and technology.

b) The second is *cross-national, horizontal, transversal, contemporary, synchronic* and *spatial*: it examines the health systems as the co-exist at a given moment.

This examination is often illuminating as it permits us to see, and to compare how the same problems of morbidity, given the same theories and conceptions of illness, are approached and resolved in different contexts: for example, the financing of health services. But here again a caution imposes itself: the transferability of patterns or arrangements generated in one cultural milieu is often limited given the different cultures into which such transfers are proposed.

For example, there has been a great deal of interest in the United States in the Canadian experiment in health care given the fact that Canada has insured health services to the entire population, while spending only 7 to 8 percent of its GNP, whereas the United States spends about 14 per cent of its GNP, and close to 40 million persons do not have health insurance, but must depend on welfare, charity or nothing. And Canada is a society with which Americans share a great deal in common: an Anglo-Saxon culture and heritage, the same language (with the exception of Québec), a democratic system, a federal structure and a balance between the federal government and the provinces in one case, the states in the other. And yet as Glaser has pointed out, the Canadian experiment is largely irrelevant to the American scene given different political cultures. In this respect, he suggests the European health systems, with their statutory coverage are a more appropriate model (Glaser, 1989).

6. The Utility of the Study of Images of Health

It is in the above-mentioned optic that we can refer to representations or images of health as an integral part of the culture of every society: their origins go very far back in time. Naturally these representations have been affected or modified by developments in scientific medicine; but they retain nevertheless their individual identity. Not only do they influence the population in its health maintenance behavior, but also affect care seeking, in its decision to consult or not consult physicians, other health personnel or healers and others considered officially as marginal. At the same time, there is every indication that the culture of a society does influence also physicians.

To conclude, let us go back very briefly to the importance of health in recalling the individual and the collective aspects of illness on the capacity of the individual to perform his or her social roles. We would like simply to add, as d'Houtaud demonstrates (Chapters 3 and 4) that health permits the individual to perform two types of roles

   a) The *instrumental* role, defined earlier, designates the fact that the individual is part of a network of mutual

obligations which are important for the functioning of
society or the group.

b)   But there is also the *expressive* aspect of roles, i.e parts of
the individual's life and activities, that do not have
necessarily an instrumental purpose, but allow him to
enjoy life, to amuse himself, to engage in sports, to relax.
Health contributes, in this manner, to the quality of life,
independently of the functional obligations of different
roles.

One of the important contributions of d'Houtaud is to have
demonstrated that the equilibrium between the expressive and
instrumental aspects of roles is different according to the socio-
occupational position of individuals. In the *lower social classes* or classes
with little income, health is seen primarily in instrumental terms.
Health is what permits members of these classes to earn their daily
bread by fulfilling their obligations and obeying orders of members of
higher classes. In the higher levels of society, on the other hand health
is seen as an important element of the *good life* and in these classes the
expressive aspect plays a much more important role than in the others.

Whether seen in its instrumental or expressive aspect, *health
occupies a fundamental place in the life* and the pre-occupations of man: it
influences directly or indirectly the functioning, indeed the very
existence of the social system. It is a key element.

Chapter 11

Some Issues and Questions on Health Care: Socio-Economic and Political Strategies in Health Systems

1. Presentation

The health system, as we noted in the previous chapter, reflects cultural images of health as well as the universal and cultural aspects of science and technology. These are transformed, adapted and applied for use in the health system. But, as we already noted, each society has its particular culture, its traditions, its manners of acting, its values: all these particular elements (by contrast with the universal aspect of science) put their imprint on the health system and on the practices of its personnel.

2. Before Modern Medicine

It is important, as part of the background, to examine what happened before and to remember how life, health, sickness and death were seen earlier. One should not think that **the scientific, positivistic and objective approach to illness** was universal and has always existed. On the contrary, this approach is *quite recent*. Or rather, that conception, which was only embryonic or marginal in the past, became dominant only in the XXth century.

In the past, people usually believed that the real life began at death. Life on earth was but preparation or prelude to what lay in the beyond. *Religion* played a preponderant role in society; priests and other religious specialists held strong powers as a result of these beliefs in the after-life. Priests, for example, defined the acts that people must perform to gain salvation and to obtain entry into paradise. Health and illness were often defined in religious or in moral terms, illness being a punition or part of divine retribution. In order to ensure a cure or to save a life, people accomplished acts of contrition or made sacrifices. Indeed, they "negotiated" with divine powers, saying, in effect, that they would do this or that to please the divinities or God, in exchange for an intervention and help in sickness. As we noted earlier, the religious aspect has not completely disappeared in the XXth century, and is particularly invoked in grave illnesses and death. In fact, one asks God, religion or philosophy to provide meaning to phenomena (an "unfair" or inexplicable death, for example) that science and medicine are not able to provide.

Generally speaking, the transformations of society and of medicine in the last hundred years or so have been dramatic. The achievements of medicine, backed by science which has become the new divinity, have immeasurably increased the power of man and of science and, in this case, the power of the physician. The physician, the one who is seen as applying science and often achieving "miracles", has displaced the priest and other religious persons from the powerful position they occupied earlier. What the physician's actions signify (symbolically, of course) is that perhaps there is no life after death; in any case, that life is a one-opportunity thing, and the physician, with his science and his techniques, has the power to improve both the quality of that life and its length. Indeed, one of the revolutionary phenomena of the last hundred years has been the dramatic increase in the life expectancy of the population. Although a great deal of that increase has not been the result of medical progress as much as of improvements in life condition, medicine receives a great deal of the credit for it.

Seen in that light, *the health system and physicians have attained great power and an extraordinary position in contemporary society,* a legitimacy well supported by legislative acts and the political clout that give allopathic medicine a kind of monopoly (not absolute, by all means) on the treatment of illness and of pain. It is therefore not surprising that this kind of power and that prestige are the cause for a counter-attack or rather **sharp criticism of contemporary medicine** and medical practices. This critique is, in our opinion, the product, half of jealousy, half of disappointment, at what medicine can accomplish in spite of its many claims. It can perhaps best be expressed in the work of Ivan Illich, particularly in his *Medical Nemesis*. His major themes (and there are many sub-themes) is that medicine is a fraud perpetrated against mankind: that its claims of curing, of reducing suffering and lengthening life are mendacious and illusory, that medicine and physicians (particularly those who work in hospitals) are dangerous to man's health. He writes, for example, that the hospital presents an enormous risk to those who enter it, risks that are related to the very dangerous nature of the hospital itself and not only to the condition for which the individual is admitted. What we see in Illich (and in others who have attacked the medical establishment) is in some respects similar to what Martin Luther had claimed in the XVIth century when he took on the Catholic Church, its monopoly on obtaining grace and its corruption. Luther advised the population to establish a direct relationship with God, by-passing the Church and the priests. And Illich suggests that *people themselves take hold of their health*, and not depend on physicians whom he calls, in general, inapt or incapable. It may be interesting to note that Illich wrote his book originally in Spanish, where the same word *salud* designates both salvation (in the religious sense) and health. The book may also reflect the grief, expressed by a Catholic priest, at the loss, on the part of the Church, of its important role in dealing with sickness, suffering and death.

These contemporary critiques of medicine obviously exaggerate to make a point. One must, nonetheless, recognize the existence of that reaction against medicine as an all-powerful institution, with a tendency toward arrogance, and a disinclination to question the validity and the value of what it does. This reaction, in our opinion, is important, when it is *a question of judging the position and the legitimacy of the health system*. Let us imagine finally what would happen if the population in general were totally convinced of the truth of the Illich thesis: i.e. that contact with medicine, physicians, hospitals can cause more harm than good. Would then people, under these circumstances, turn to a doctor, to be hospitalized when sick? A situation like this did appear in the Soviet Union when the notorious *Doctors' Case* broke out in 1953. The case (which after Stalin's death was shown to be a complete fabrication) was that Soviet physicians who treated highly placed political personalities had engaged in *medical sabotage:* they had hastened or caused the death of several persons through contra-indicated, harmful regimens. In other words, instead of saving lives, they committed murder under cover of medical acts. As a result, many in the population lost confidence in medicine and physicians, were afraid of going to polyclinics and hospitals, were fearful of being poisoned by prescribed drugs. We did mention the question of legitimacy in the previous chapter as an important, indeed, an indispensable, asset and resource. This again demonstrates the tenuousness and the conditional nature of legitimacy, particularly that of powerful institutions, like medicine in the contemporary world.

3. Political Aspects of the Health System

As a sub-system of society, the health system, by its very nature and because of the important functions with which it is entrusted by society, has a **political aspect** which it cannot escape. The question we must pose for a comprehensive analysis is the degree of power it has vis-à-vis other sub-systems (education, for example), and more particularly vis-à-vis society at large. There are in this domain many variations that again contradict the idea of convergence. It is usually among *physicians that this power can be located. In many societies, physicians and their associations exercise a very profound control on all aspects of the health system.* They are also able, in many instances, to impose their views and to influence the legislature and politicians. In other countries, there is some kind of equilibrium among different groups inside the health system, and which determine the power and the influence of that sector. For example, a situation in which physicians, on the one hand, and insurance funds, on the other, are in constant negotiations with each other, with the State playing the role of arbiter, more or less neutral, as is the case in Germany.

In other countries, the individuals themselves (as patients or potential patients) have a certain delegated power to influence society and its health policies (Great Britain, for example). Finally, *in some countries of the totalitarian type, the health system and physicians have almost no power:* they are subordinate to the State, being often the creation and the creature of the State, and having no counter-wailing power (as is, or was the case, in the Soviet Union).

But the power enjoyed nowadays by physicians in many countries is under attack and is apparently weakening. One of the reasons is without doubt the increasing costs of health care, with the third parties (the State, the organs of Social Security, insurance carriers) attempting to put a brake on these cost increases. Physicians are seen as being the major causes of these increases. Even in the hospitals, where in earlier days they were all powerful in deciding what could be done, they see their powers of decision being gradually eroded by the "bean counters", by those who administer the budget and by administrators (who increasingly are not, as they used to be, physicians themselves).This administrative structure increasingly makes decisions that, in the past, were the exclusive domain of physicians. From this phenomenon, one can distinguish, in a very preliminary fashion, at least four different models concerning the role and the power of the physician in the world today, and perhaps tomorrow.

a) The **professional** model is the one of private or *liberal* medicine. It is the traditional model, and implies an almost total autonomy for the physician.

b) The **bureaucratic** model is one in which the physician is, little by little, transformed into a *functionary*, an employee. His actions are increasingly limited or dictated by bureaucrats and bureaucratic norms: how many patients to be seen? What medicines can be prescribed? Under what circumstances can one deliver a medical excuse or certificate of illness? The bureaucratic model means that the physician is not working by himself, but is part of an organization or structure, a hospital or a clinic, and that this organization has certain claims on his professional activities.

c) The **proletarian** model is one in which the physician does not have, any more, the initiative and the choices of the *bureaucratic* model, however limited these may be. In this model, which could perhaps just as well be called the "employee" model, the physician is reduced, to a large extent, to the carrying out of orders and assignments. The word "proletarianization" implies that the physician does not have the control of the tools or the Means of Medical Production. Some think that, pushed to its logical conclusion, the fate of physicians will move in that direction.

d) The **commercial** model is the one in which the physician defines himself as an *entrepreneur* in a commercial market situation, competing with other entrepreneurs for a share of that market. This model does not exclude (as can already be seen in the United States) the use of advertising.

4. Specialization and Internal Differentiation

We have spoken of certain tendencies that manifest themselves in the power (or in the absence thereof) of the health system and particularly of physicians. A closely related question is that **of the solidarity and of the corporate nature of the medical world and the medical profession:** i.e. of its capacity to act in concert to defend its interests.

One could say that in the XIXth century, most of the physicians had *common interests* because they all were, more or less, in the same situation. Toward the end of the XXth century, the situation has radically changed. There is first the trend toward *specialization* which we have already touched upon. This leads to a diversification of medical practices and acts *against the solidarity* that once came from similar medical practices. In addition, and acting against the unity of the medical body, there is now a multiplicity of situations in which physicians exercise their art. In contemporary society we see physicians working in private practice, either solo or group; then there is the practice of medicine in the Health Maintenance Organizations, as is the case primarily in the United States, in which the physician receives a fixed stipend or salary, which may be increased to the degree that the HMO saves money through physicians' decisions and actions, for example through a reduction in costly hospitalization and the use of cheaper treatment methods, such as day-surgery. Finally there is strictly salaried practice. It seems quite clear that these differences contribute not to a commonality of interests but rather to a diversity. This is a relatively new factor that contributes (or will contribute) to decrease the solidarity of physicians, and consequently to reduce their political power, either inside the health system or in the confrontation of the health system and the rest of society.

There is yet another consequence of specialization which we already briefly mentioned. It is the process of specialization and differentiation observed not only within the physicians, but also among nurses and other personnel. This specialization is itself partly the result of the accumulation of knowledge and of technical progress. *This process of specialization has its advantages*, in that physicians are able to perform very complicated and sometimes daring interventions which they never could do alone. The downside of this process is the need to assemble, into a meaningful "product", the increasingly splintered and divided activities of an increasingly large numbers of individuals, both professional and non-professional. This then is a problem of integration in a complex division of medical labor, or the assembly of a large number of small pieces or inputs. One could use, in this respect as an illustration, the following metaphor: an automobile manufacturer wants to assemble vehicles of excellent quality in large numbers and at the most reasonable costs. For this purpose, he builds or establishes a series of factories or sub-assembly plants where the different component parts of the automobile are manufactured in large numbers, accurately and at low cost. In his enthusiasm however, the manufacturer has forgotten to build a final assembly plant where all the pieces are to be put together into a usable product; the result is that he has large inventories of separate pieces that have no utility, no value, and do not constitute a finished product. This is of course a hyperbolic example. It helps however to alert us to the technical, and indeed to the clinical dangers of a division of medical labor when that division or differentiation is not accompanied by a parallel process of integration or de-differentiation. Calls for a return to general practice or to family medicine are a reflection of the malaise created by super specialization.

There is yet another aspect of that parceling of the medical product: the large quantity of personnel who participate in it, and *the fate of the patient*. Beyond the technical questions raised above concerning the integration of processes (for example, errors of communications) and which may have serious or sometimes fatal consequences, there is the emotional state of the patient. In essence alone with suffering, and with the association of illness with disability and death, he or she is facing a complex and often incomprehensible world of machinery and technology and a large number of specialists and technicians who speak a language unknown to the patient. He remains isolated, ignorant, alienated and anxious.

In that situation, the classical role of the therapist tends to recede and be replaced by the esoteric one of the technician.

It is therefore not surprising, under these circumstances, that healers, *Christian Scientists*, quacks and others, are so attractive to many: they compensate for the technical coldness and impersonality by providing personal and emotional supports to those who are sick and anxious, and need to be comforted and reassured.

5. Technologies and Personnel in Medicine

Following our discussion on specialization, we want briefly to turn our attention to **technology in medicine**. The classical equation of labor, capital and know-how as it applies to production is equally relevant to the world of medicine. Medical capital (technology) is however quite different from the one found in the industrial world.

In industry, the purpose of equipment and of non-human sources of energy is primarily *the replacement of labor by machines*. When a new piece of equipment is proposed to an industrialist, the first question is its cost, in how much time the cost will be recouped or amortized, and by how much will it reduce the expense of production compared to the use of labor. If the cost is acceptable, the industrialist has an advantage in adopting the new equipment to reduce the amount of labor. The ideal, in fact, would be a plant where only robots would work. Machines do not go on strike, they do not make demands, they do not have families, they do not become sick (though they need maintenance and eventually replacement), and they work, when needed, without sleeping and without interruption.

Medical technology is different in many respects. It allows the physician and the health system to do what could not be done yesterday. Let us take the case of dialysis. Up to the day is was developed and successfully tested, the physician in good conscience could say to the patient: "I am sorry, but medical knowledge cannot do anything for you". But from the very moment when this kind of equipment was demonstrated to work, the physician could not, in good conscience, any more say that medicine had no answer to the patient's problem. One then passed from the innocence of ignorance (and impotence) to the culpability of the possible or the potential. From that time on, the only question is access to such equipment, hence pressures on society and on medicine to purchase such equipment. This is quite different from the purchasing of industrial equipment. It is a question of life itself, of suffering, of conditions which really do not have a price. Thus *the adoption of medical technology obeys a logic that is quite different from that of industry*. But it raises another series of questions to which we alluded earlier: costs.

In the industrial world, technology, equipment is *substitutive*: as we have seen, it replaces labor. In the domain of health, certainly in some cases equipment is substitutive (for example injection needles that are disposable eliminate the need for personnel to resterilize or to sharpen them). But in most instances (the example of dialysis or scanners), this equipment is *additive*. It does not lead to a reduction of costs but, as we already pointed out, to the *need for more personnel*. Thus medical equipment is both labor and capital intensive, and contributes to increase overall health costs. One could of course advance the argument that in the final analysis it prolongs the life of people, that society and patients benefit, that such benefits could be translated into a final reduction of costs. That may be possible, but a calculation of cost-benefits in those terms is so complicated and implicate so many variables that it is difficult to reach firm conclusions. But what is increasingly apparent, and to some ominous and distasteful, is that health care, particularly the use of high-cost equipment will eventually be rationed and indeed already is. This opens up the whole and complex issue of the bases of this rationing which will probably, by the end of this century, become one of the burning social, political and ideological questions.

6. Changes in the Health System in the 20th Century

Health care and **the place the health system occupies in modern society** have become important issues toward the end of the XXth century.

If we take a historical perspective and go back to the XIXth century, we find that at that time medicine could not do very much about illness and premature death. Hospitals were refuges where the poor and the sick could find a bed or some straw, and something to keep them from starving; it was a place where people went to die rather than to get well. The health system as such was rudimentary and consumed but a very small amount of available societal resources. The situation changed dramatically in the XXth century. It is only after 1910 or 1912 according to Henderson that a random patient with a random disease consulting a physician chosen at random had more than one chance in two of benefitting from the encounter. From that time on, due to scientific progress and discoveries in laboratories and clinics, *medicine has become effective in many cases*. The health system which in the XIXth century was not important has become one of the most active, most visible, and costliest sectors of society. At he present time, every society is concerned with this development: the political sector in particular. In many countries (particularly industrial and urban ones) the State has made a formal commitment to the population that health care was a right of citizenship, and not a privilege that only the few could afford to purchase. But it is also clear that no State is in the position of creating a health system to fulfill this promise or commitment. One cannot start *de novo*.

And from this point on, the question is of the manner in which the State or society can manipulate, transform, expand the system that already exists, and how it can come to terms with health personnel (physicians in particular) who often object against the interference of the State in its professional matters. And finally, the phenomenon that one observes practically everywhere, *is the weight and the importance that the health system occupies in contemporary society.*

It should be also noted that this may be due to a particularity of Occidental or Western culture with its optimism, with its activism, with its hubris that holds that with good will and determination, with sufficient resources (human and material) man can surmount most obstacles, including illness and premature mortality. This is a trait that in general terms distinguishes Western from Oriental or Eastern culture(s), or even from Western culture of a century or two ago. These cultures had a tendency to accept disease and premature mortality with resignation as foreordained by a superior power or by fate. It was therefore arrogant to try to fight against that power. Thus disease was punishment meted by God and man should accept it as such. The attitude nowadays, in the West particularly but in the world at large increasingly, is that *research is capable of eventually resolving all problems of health*. This optimism has, of late, been tempered particularly as a result of the work of René Dubos who in his book *Mirage of Health* (1960) maintains that a world without illness is not possible, and that as man finds solutions and cures for one disease after another, new ones are bound to take their place. The AIDS epidemic (which appeared after Dubos wrote his seminal work) seems to bear him out.

7. The Interventions of the State in the Health Sector

Let us go back to the role of the State.

a) **The role of the State** becomes increasingly preponderant in the health system. And certainly the growth of the latter gives it an increasing political importance. The fact that *the health system absorbs an ever increasing portion of the Gross National Product* has become in most countries a subject of alarm. Indeed the resources of any social formation are never unlimited: what is allocated to the health system must often be taken from another sector.

b) It should also be noted that the question is often posed of **the utility of the health system** : does society receive enough value from that system in exchange of what it spends for it (Peterson et al., 1967; Powles, 1973). Would it not be wiser to hold a part of these resources and to rechannel them toward other sectors that would contribute more, though perhaps indirectly, to raise the health level of the population (better housing, for example)?

c) The promise or commitment to the population regarding **health care** done by most industrial states, which we have noted earlier, has changed the population's attitude toward that care: it is now regarded as a right of citizenship and not a personal object of consumption that one could or could not afford according to income or social position. Health care in most societies has rejoined education as a basic right. And the population tends, under these circumstances, to demand more and more, particularly as that population tends to live longer, and thus to need more care of all types. And this of course poses a dilemma to State and society, since this promise may begin to encroach on other sectors that are seen as just as deserving. This then leads almost everywhere to attempts to find ways and means to reduce   costs: co-payments, deductibles, privatization or re-privatization (as in the case of Great Britain).

d) The promise of health care on a universal basis and the establishment of arrangements to fulfill that promise (insurance, Social Security) are usually based on the principle of **equity**. But this equity before illness and death is of course never realized or realizable, in spite of the promises of the State or other institutions in charge of health care and social welfare. For the differences in health levels and in mortality from groups to groups in the same society (by socio-economic class, by race, by ethnicity) reflect social differences and stratification that health care simply cannot eradicate.

e) At the same time, there exists a cause of morbidity and mortality against which the health system finds it difficult to struggle, the **voluntary health risks:** *alcoholism, smoking, drug abuse, sedentarity and obesity,* etc. These are problems that are solidly anchored in society and in culture (which A d'HOUTAUD has well explored) and which are not easily resolved. On the other side, one must also realize that alcohol and tobacco sales in most countries are *important sources of revenues for the State.* Thus a significant decrease in the use of alcohol and tobacco might have a pernicious effect on the economic life of the society, as paradoxical as it might seem on first sight. Thus often States hesitate to take draconian measures in that regard.

We have raised here some critical issues and questions concerning health and the health system. In conclusion, we can simply add that **this system is in constant state of flux,** and that the health system (and health problems) in the next century are likely to be as different as those of the present century are from the XIXth. And this state of flux comes not only *from the dynamism of medicine itself,* but also from the society it serves and *from scientific progress:* three elements that are narrowly linked to each other.

Recapitulation of Part IV

· In chapter 10 we proceded, using a functional and structural approach, to an examination of the importance of health for the organism that is society. The departure point was the significance of social roles for the functioning of the social system; then we examined the impact or the consequences of the incapacity to perform these roles because of illness, pain, handicap and the ultimate incapacity of death.

In this optic, the health system is seen as a socio-cultural response to the **problems caused society by incapacity,** while it is at the same time a response to the personal and the subjective problems of those who are affected by illness and trauma.

We described the major elements of the health system. They include one external component (health services), and two internal components allowing the system to function and to reproduce itself: on the one hand, arrangements allowing the health system to recruit and to educate personnel to replace those who leave it (retirement, illness, death); and, on the other hand, arrangements that elaborate and apply general scientific knowledge, as well as technology, to health problems. In our opinion, medical research is the most dynamic, let's say revolutionary, part of the contemporary health system.

Since the health system does not produce its own resources, we then examined the external supports indispensable to the functioning of the health system. They are 1) economic inputs; 2) human resources (personnel); 3) social legitimacy; and 4) knowledge (an essentially cultural input).

An understanding of the health system can benefit from a comparative examination of health systems in the world. This examination leads to two hypotheses that are not necessarily contradictory: the idea of the convergence of these systems under the impulse of the utilization of similar knowledge and technological means; and a more nuanced approach according to which each health system is the product of a dialectical tension and synthesis between the universal aspects of this scientific knowledge and the particular aspects of each society and culture. It is in that optic that we can discern the capital importance of images of health as a component of the culture of each society.

In chapter 11, we rapidly examined certain questions posed by the development of the health system to contemporary society. We looked first at the sharp criticisms directed against it (including those that maintain that the health system, physicians and hospitals are dangerous to health), and the reasons for such attacks. We then examined the political aspects of the health system in any society as well as the political roles of physicians and their associations, and the possible evolution of these roles in four directions: the professional model, the bureaucratic model, the proletarian model, and the commercial model. We then looked at the internal and important problems of the health system like specialization and differentiation, and their implications for health care and the fate of patients. The ever increasing role of technology and the questions this poses were mentioned. Finally, we tried to bring out the historical evolution of the health system from the XIXth century on and the ever-increasing role of the State in that sector of society. In conclusion, we pointed to the constant state of flux in that domain: it originates not only in the dynamics of the system itself, but in society and scientific/technological advances.

BIBLIOGRAPHY

ABEL-SMITH, B. (1976) *Value for Money in Health Services: A Comparative Study.* New York: St Martin. Press.

ALTENSTETTER, C., and HAYWOOD, S.C. (in press) *From rhetoric to reality: Comparative health policy and the new right.* London: The Macmillan Press Ltd.

ANDERSEN, R., SMEDBY, B., and ANDERSON, O.W. (1970), *Medical care use in Sweden and the U.S. - A comparative analysis of systems and behavior.* Chicago: Center for Health Administration Studies.

ANDERSON, O.W. (1966), "Health services systems in the United States and other contries - Critical comparisons", *Medical Care, Social and Organizational Aspects.*

ANDERSON, O.W. (1967), "Toward a framework for analyzing health services systems with examples from selected countries", *Social and Economic Administration.*

ANDERSON, O.W. (1972) *Health Care: Can there be equity? The United States, Sweden an England.* New York: Wiley.

ARMER, M. (1973). "Methodological Problems and Possibilities in Comparative Research" Pp 49-79 in *Comparative Social Research: Methodological Problems and Strategies,* edited by Michael Armer and Allen D. Grimshaw. New York: Wiley.

ARMER, M., and GRIMSHAW, A.D. eds. (1973). Comparative Social Research: *Methodological Problems and Strategies.* New York: Wiley.

BABSON, J. (1972), *Health care delivery systems: A multi-national survey.* London: Pitman Medical.

BADGLEY, R. et al. (1971), "International studies of health manpower: A sociologic perspective" *Medical Care,* May-June.

BASTIDE, R. (1971) Protestantisme et Médecine de Folk *Revista de Ethnografia,* 15 (2).

BATES, E.M. (1983). *Health Systems and Public Scrutiny: Australia, Britain and the United States.* London and Canberra: Croom Helm.

BAUDEROT, J. (1976) Ivan Illich: l'Ethique médicale et l'esprit de la société industrielle. *Esprit,* 44 (454) 288-314.

BENVENISTE, E. (1969) Le vocabulaire des institutions européennes.

BICE,Th., and **WHITE, K.L.** (1969), "Factors related to the use of health services: An international comparative study", *Medical Care*, VII (2).

BICE, Th., and **WHITE K.L.** (1971), "Cross-national comparative research on the utilization of medical services", *Medical Care*, May-June.

BLENDON, R.J. (1989) "Three systems; A comparative survey", *Health Management Quarterly*, 11 (1) 1-10.

BOLDERSON, H. (1989) "Comparing Social Policies: Some Problems of methods and the case of social security benefits in Australia, Britain and the USA, *Journal of Social Policy*, 17 (3).

BOLTANSKI, L. (1971) Les usages sociaux du corps. *Annales*, janvier-février, 205-233.

BOUET, M. (1968) *Signification du sport*. Paris, 620 pages.

BTESH, B. (1965) "International Research in the Organisation of Medical Care", *Medical Care* 3: 41-46.

BUI, D.H.D. (1988) *The Future of Health Care and Health Systems in the Industrialized Societies*. New York: Praeger.

CALNAN, M. (1987) *Health and illness: the lay perspective*. Tavistock Publications, London and NewYork, 198 pages.

CHARRON, R.C. (1963), *Health services, health insurance and their interrelationship*. Ottawa: Canadian Department of National Health and Welfare.

CHASE-DUNN, C.K. (1979)."Comparative Research on World-System Characteristics", *International Studies Quarterley*, 23: 601-23.

CHASE-DUNN, C.K. (1982). "The Uses of Formal Comparative Research on Dependency Theory and the World-System. Perspective". Pp 117-137 in *The New International Economy*, edited by Harry Makler, Alberto Martinelli, and Neil Smelser. London: Sage.

CHASE-DUNN, C.K., PALLAS A.M., and **KANTOR, J.** (1982). "Old and New Research Designs for Studying the World System: A Research Note", *Comparative Political Studies* 15: 341-56.

CHASTAING, M. (1951) *La philosophie de Virginia Woolf*. Paris, 1951

CHASTAING, M. (1976) Psychologie des jurons. *Journal de Psychologie*, 34, 443-468

CHASTAING, M., and **ABDI H.,** (1980) Psychologie des injures. *Journal de Psychologie*, 1, 31-62.

COE, R. (1970), *Sociology of Medicine*, New York: Mc Graw Hill.

CUMONT, F. (1929) *Les religions orientales dans le paganisme romain*. Paul Geuthner, Paris.

CURRER, C., and **STACEY, M.** (1986) *Concepts of Health, Illness and Disease: a comparative perspective*. Berg, Spa, Hamburg, NewYork, 324 pages.

d'HOUTAUD, A. (1975, a) Comment les patients perçoivent leur médecin et ses relations avec eux. *Revue internationale d'éducation pour la santé*, 18 (2) 120-142, et (3) 173-188.

d'HOUTAUD, A. (1975, b) Comment les patients parlent spontanément de leur médecin et de la médecine. *Revue internationale d'éducation pour la santé*, 18 (4) 241-256.

d'HOUTAUD, A. (1976) Les représentations de la santé, recherches dans un centre de bilan de santé en Lorraine. *Revue internationale d'éducation pour la santé*, 19, 99-118 et 173-188.

d'HOUTAUD, A. (1977, a) *Recherches en Lorraine sur les facteurs psychosociaux de la santé* (3 tomes). Thèse de doctorat ès Lettres et Sciences humaines, Diffusion par la librairie H. CHAMPION. Paris.

d'HOUTAUD, A. (1977, b) Ce que les gens attendent du médecin et de la médecine au sujet de leur santé. *Cahiers de Sociologie et de Démographie médicales*, n° 316, 41-46.

d'HOUTAUD, A. (1978, a) L'image de la santé dans une population lorraine. Approche psychosociologique des représentations de la santé. *Revue d'épidémiologie et de santé publique*, 26, 299-320.

d'HOUTAUD, A. (1978, b) Santé et salutation: pour une approche historique et sémantique du terme santé. *Revue internationale d'éducation pour la santé*, 21 (4), 277-283.

d'HOUTAUD, A. (1979) Santé et salut: pour une approche historique et sémantique du terme santé. *Revue internationale d'éducation pour la santé*, 22 (1), 49-56.

d'HOUTAUD, A. (1981) Nouvelles recherches sur les représentations de la santé. *Revue internationale d'éducation pour la santé*, 24 (3), 322.

d'HOUTAUD, A. (1982) La rage, sa charge émotive. *Revue Française de la Santé Publique*, 19, 410.

d'HOUTAUD, A., and **FIELD M.G.** (1984) The image of health: variations in perception by social class in a French population. *Sociology of Health and Illness*, 6 (1), 30-60.

d'HOUTAUD, A. and **FIELD M.G.** (1986) *New Research on the image of health* in CURRER C.(supra), 235-255.

d'HOUTAUD, A., and **FIELD M.G.** (1989 a) *La santé: approche sociologique de ses représentations et de ses fonctions dans la société.* Presses Universitaires de Nancy.

d'HOUTAUD, A., and **FIELD M.G.,** and **GUEGUEN R.** (1989 b) *Les représentations de la santé: bilan actuel, nouveaux développements.* Collection des Colloques de l'I.N.S.E.R.M

d'HOUTAUD, A., POULIZAC H., and **SENAULT R.** (1973) A la recherche d'une pédagogie de la santé: enquêtes d'opinions et d'attitudes. A propos d'un bilan familial de la santé. *Revue Internationale d'éducation pour la santé (fascicule séparé)*, 48 pages.

DAVIS, A. (1979). "An Unequivocal Change of Policy: Prevention, Health and Medical Sociology",*Social Science and Medicine*, 13a:129.

DEMIGUEL, J.M., (1975)". A Framework for the Study of National Health Systems", *Inquiry*, supplement to vol. 12, 2, 10-24.

DUBOS, R. (1960), *Mirage of health*, London: Allen and Unwin.

DUMBAUGH, K., and NEUHAUSER, D. (1979), "International Comparisons of Health Services: Where are We "? *Social Science and Medicine*, Vol. 13 b, 221-223.

DUPRAT, G.L. (1930) La contrainte sanitaire. *Revue Internationale de Sociologie*, 38...

DURKHEIM, E. (1972) *Le suicide, étude de sociologie*. Alcan, 2ème Edition, Paris

ELDER, J. W. (1976), "Comparative Cross-National Methodology", Pp. 209-230 in *Annual Review of Sociology*, vol.2, edited by Alex Inkeles. Palo Alto. CA: Annual Reviews, Inc.

ELLING, R.E. (1980), *Cross-National Study of Health Systems*. New Brunswick: Transaction Books.

ERNOUT, A. et MEILLET, A. (1959) *Dictionnaire étymologique de la langue latine*. Klincksieck, Paris.

EVANG, K., STARK-MURRAY, D., and LEAR, W.J. (1963), *Medical care and family security*. Englewood Cliffs: N.J. Prentice Hall.

FABREGA, H. (1976), "The Functions of Medical Care Systems: A Logical Analysis", *Perspective in Biology and Medicine* 20: 109-118.

FIELD, M. G. (1970), " The medical system and industrial society : Structural changes and internal differentiation in American medicine", in Allan Sheldon, Frank Baker and Curt McLaughlin (Eds.), *Systems and medical care*, Cambridge: Massachussetts Institute of Technology Press, pp. 143-181.

FIELD, M. G. (1971), "Stability and change in the medical system: Medicine in the industrial society", in Alex Inkeles and Bernard Barber (Eds). *Stability and social change*. Boston: Little-Brown, pp. 30-60.

FIELD, M. G. (1971), "The health care system of industrialized society: The disappearance of the general practitioner and some implications", in Everett I. Mendelsohn, Judith P. Swazey and Irene Taviss(eds), *Human Aspects of biological innovation*, Cambridge: Harvard University Press, pp. 156-180.

FIELD, M. G. (1974), "Prospects for the comparative sociology of medicine: An effort at conceptualization," *Current Research in Sociology*, edited by Margaret Archer. Supplementary Volume I, 147-183.

FIELD, M. G. (1987), "Reflections on Medical Technology as a Special Type of Capital," *International Journal of Technology Assessment in Health Care*, 3, 275-290.

FIELD, M. G. (1988), " L'évolution comparée des systèmes de santé convergence, diversité et recoupements", *Médecine et Hygiène*, 46, 422-430.

FIELD, M. G. (1989), *Success and Crisis in National Health Systems: A Comparative Approach*, London: Routledge.

FINIFTER, Bernard M. (1977). "The Robustness of Cross-Cultural Findings", *Annals New York Academy of Sciences* 285:151-84.

FLORA, P., and **HEIDENHEIMER, J.** (eds) (1979) *The Development of the Welfare State in Europe and America*. New Jersey: New Jersey Brunswick.

FORM, W.H. (1976), "Blue Collar Stratification: *Autoworkers in Four Countries* ", Princeton NJ: Princeton University Press.

FORM, W.H. (1979), "Comparative Industrial Sociology and the Convergence Hypothesis".pp 1-25 in *Annual Review of Sociology*, vol. 5. edited by Alex Inkeles. Palo Alto. CA: Annual Reviews. Ine.

FRY, J. (1969), *Medicine in three societies: A Comparison of medical care in the USSR, USA and UK*. New York: American Elsevier Publishing Co.

FRY, J., and **FARNDALE, W.A.J.** (Eds.) (1972), *International medical care: A comparison and evaluation of medical care services throughout the world*. Wallingford. Pa.: Washington Square East.

GLASER, W.A. (1978) *Health Insurance Bargaining: Foreign Lessons for Americans*, New York: Gardner Press and John Riley.

GLASER, W.A. (1977) "The Process of cross-national survey research", In 1. Aazalai and R. Patrella, (eds) *Cross-National Comparative Survey Research*. New York: Pergamon Press, 403-435.

GLASER, W. A. (1969), *The social settings of medical care*. New York: Atherton Press.

GLASER, W. A. (1970), *Paying the doctor: Systems of remuneration and their effects*. Baltimore: John Hopkins Press.

GLASER, W.A. (1990) "*Comparative Research Methods*", Report prepared for the symposium on The International Comparison of Social Security Policies and Systems, Paris 13-15 June organised by the French service for planning and financing of research of the Ministry of Social affairs (MIRE) in cooperation with the International social security association (ISSA).

GOFFMAN, E. (1973) *La mise en scène de la vie quotidienne*. Edition de Minuit, Paris, 1973

GRABLE, H., and **THIEL, G.** (1989) *Updating the fee schedule for physician reimbursement: Comparative analysis of selected experience abroad and of policy options for the United States*. Washingtion, DC: PPRC.

GRAWITZ, M. (1976) *Méthodes des sciences sociales*. Dunod, Paris

GRIMSHAW, A.D. (1973), "Comparative Sociology: In What Ways Different from other Sociologies?" pp 3-48 in *Comparative Social*

Research: Methodological Problems and Strategies, edited by Michael Armer and Allen D. Grimshaw. New York: Wiley.

HANNAY, D. (1979), *The Symptom Iceberg: A Study in Community Health* London: Routledge and Kegan Paul.

HERZLICH, C. (1973) *Health and Illness*, Academic Press, London.

HERZLICH, C. (1979) *Santé et Maladie, analyse d'une représentation sociale.* Mouton Paris, la Haye.

HERZLICH, C. (1973) *Health and illness: A Social Psychological Analysis*, London: Academic Press.

HERZLICH, C., and PIERRET J. (1984), *Malades d'hier, Malades d'Aujourd'hui*, Paris: Payot.

HOPKINS, T.K., and WALLERSTEIN, I. (1967) "The comparative study of national societies". *Social Science Information* 6: 25-58.

ILLICH, I. (1975) *Némésis médicale.* Seuil, Paris.

INKELES, A., and SMITH, D.H. (1974). *Becoming Modern: Individual Change in Six Developing Countries.* Cambridge. MA: Harvard University Press.

KASER, M. (1976) *Health Care in the Soviet Union and Eastern Europe.* Boulder, Colorado: Westview Press.

KOHN, M (1987), "Cross-National research as an Analytic Strategy", *American Sociological Review*, 52, 6, 713-731.

KOHN, M (1981), "Personality, Occupation and Social Stratification: A Frame of Reference." pp.267-97 in *Research in Social Stratification and Mobility: A Research Annual.* Vol.1, edited by Donald J. Treiman and Robert V. Robinson. Greenwich, CT:JAI Press.

KOHN, M (1985) "Unresolved Interpretive Issues in the Relationship Between Work and Personality". Paper presented at the annual meeting of the American Sociological Association, Washington. DC. August.

KOHN, M , ATSUSHI, N., SCOENBACH, C., SCHOOLER, C., and SLOMEZYNSKI, K. (1987). "Position in the Class structure and Psychological Functioning: A Comparative Analysis of the United Sates, Japan, and Poland." Paper presented at a plenary session of the Southern Sociological Society. Atlanta. April 1987, and at a USSR-US Symposium on the Social organization of Work, Vilnius, USSR, July 1987.

LE SENNE, R. (1942) *Traité de Morale.* P.U.F., Paris.

LEICHTER, H. M. (1977) "Comparative Public Policy: Problems and Prospects", *Policy Studies Journal*, Vol 5. 583-596.

LEICHTER, H. M. (1979) *A Comparative Analysis of Policy: Health Care Policy in Four Nations.* New York: Cambridge University Press.

LEICHTER, H. M. (1991) *Free to be Foolish: Politics and Health Promotion in the United States and Great Britain.* Princeton, New Jersey: Princeton University Press.

LEWITT, R. (1976) The Reorganized National Health Service. London: Croom Helm.

LIGHT, D. W. (1984) *Comparing Health Care Systems: Lessons from East Germany. Health and Illness: Critical Prespectives*, 2nd ed. Peter Conrad and Rochelle Kern, eds. New York: St-Martin Press.

LIGHT, D. W., and SCHULLER, A. (1985). *The Impact of Political Values on Health Care: The German Experience*. Cambridge: M T. Press.

LITMAN, T.J., and ROBINS L. (1971), "Comparative analysis of health care systems -A socio-political approach", *Social Science and Medicine*, 5: 573-81.

LOGAN, R.F.L. (1968), "International studies of illness and health services", *Milbank Memorial Fund Quartely*, N° 2, Part 2:126.

LYNCH, L. R. (1969). *The Cross Cultural Approach to Health Behavior*. Rutherford, New Jersey: Fairleigh Dickinson University Press.

MABRY, J.H. (1971), "International studies of health care", *Medical Care*, IX (3).

MAGET, M. (1962) *Guide d'étude directe des comportements culturels* C.N.R.S., Paris.

MAGET, M. (1968) Problèmes d'ethnographie européenne in Ethnologie générale sous la direction de J. POIRIER, pages 1247-1338 Encyclopédie de la Pléiade, Gallimard, Paris.

MAJONE, G. (1982), "Prevention and Health Standards: American, Soviet and European Models", *Journal of Health Politics, Policy and Law*, 7 (3): 629-47.

MARMOR, T. R., (1980) "American Health Planning and the Lessons of Comparative Policy Analysis", *Journal of Health Politics, Policy and Law*, Vol 5, 3, Fall 1980, 419-430.

MARSH, R.M. (1967), Comparative Sociology: A Codification of Cross-Societal Analysis. New York: Harcourt. Brace & World.

MAUSS, M. (19231925) Divisions et proportions des divisions de la sociologie. *Année sociologique*, t.2, 98-176.

MERRIEN, F.X. (1990). *The construction of the Welfare States: The Crisis of paradigms and reorganisation of social policies in France, Great Britain and the United States, 1900-1950*. Report prepared for the symposium on the International Comparison of Social Security Pollicies and Systems, Paris, 13-15 June 1990, organised by the French service for planning and financing of research, Ministry of Social Affairs (MIRE) in cooperation with the International social security association (ISSA).

MEYER, J. W., and HANNAN M.T. eds. (1979), *National Development and the World System: Educational. Economic, and Political Change, 1950-1970*. Chicago: University of Chicago Press.

MICHELAT, G. (1975) Sur l'utilisation de l'entretien nondirectif en sociologie. *Revue Française de sociologie*, 16, 229247.

MILLER, J., SLOMEZYNSKI, K., and SCHOENBERG, R.J. (1981), "Assessing Comparability of Measurement in Cross-National Research: Authoritarian-Conservatism in Different Sociocultural Settings. *Social Psychology Quarterly* 44:178-91.

MOSCOVICI, S. (1961) *La psychanalyse, son image et son public. Etude sur la représentation sociale de la psychanalyse.* P.U.F., Paris.

PEARLIN, L.I (1971), *Class Context and Family Relations: A Cross-National Study.* Boston: Little Brown.

PETER, J.P. (1971), "Les mots et les objets de la maladie", *Revue Historique* 499,1971.

PETERSON, O. L. et al. (1967), "What is the value for money in medical care?" *The Lancet.*

PFAFF, M. (1990) "Differences in health care spending across countries", *Journal of Health Politics, Policy and Law,* 15 (1), 1 68.

PLATON Les Lois Encyclopédie de la pléiade, Gallimard

POULLIER, J-P. (1990) *Health OECD.* Paris: Organisation for Economic Co-operation and Development.

POUVOURVILLE, G. de (1985) *Le paiement de l'acte médical: Une comparaison entre la France, les Etats Unis et le Québec,* Paris: Ecole Polytechnique, Centre de Recherche en Gestion.

POUVOURVILLE, G. de, (1990) *The comparative approach to health systems: regulation or self-regulation.* Report prepared for the symposium on The International Comparison of Social Security Policies and Systems, Paris, June 13-15, organised the French service for planning and financing of research of the Ministry of Social Affairs (MIRE) in cooperation with the International social security association (ISSA).

POWLES, J. (1973), "On the Limitations of Modern Medicine", *Science Medicine and Man I* (1): 1-30.

PREWORSKI, A., and TEUNE, H. (1970), *The Logic of Comparative Social Inquiry.* New York: Wiley-Interscience.

RAFFEL, M. W. (1984) *Comparative Health Systems.* University Park: Pennsylvania University Press.

RAGIN, C. (1982), "Comparative Sociology and the Comparative Method". *International Journal of Comparative Sociology* 22: 102-20.

RAGIN, C., and ZARET D. (1983). "Theory and Method in Comparative Research: Two Strategies". *Social Forces* 61:731-54.

RAMUZ, C. (1921) *Salutation paysanne.* Grasset, Paris

RODWIN, V. (1987) "Le contrôle des pouvoirs publics et des payeurs: Comparaisons internationales" in *Systèmes de santé. pouvoirs publics et financeurs: Qui contrôle quoi?* Paris, Documentation française.

RODWIN, V.G. (1984) "Comparative Health Systems: Notes on the Literature" in V.G. Rodwin, *The Health Planning Predicament :* France, Québec, England and the U.S. Berkeley: University of California Press, pp. 239-248.

ROEMER, M. I. (1967), *Hospital systems in different nations*. Geneva: World Health Organization.

ROEMER, M. I. (1969), *The organization of medical care under social security: A study based on the experience of eight countries*. Geneva: WHO.

ROEMER, M. I. (1970), "General physician services under eight national patterns", *American Journal of Public Health*, 60 (Oct.): 1893-1899.

ROEMER, M (1977) *Comparative National Policies on Health Care*. New York: Marcel Dekker.

ROKKAN, S. (1964),"Comparative Cross-National Research: The Context of Current Efforts", pp. 3-25 in *Comparing Nations:The Use of Quantitative Data in Cross-National Research*, edited by Richard I. Merritt and Stein Rokkan. New Haven. CT: Yale University Press.

SALTMAN, R. B. (1988) *International Handbook of Health Care Systems*. New York: Greenwood Press.

SCHEUCH, E. K. (1967). "Society as Context in Cross-Cultural Comparisons". *Social Science Information* 6:7-23.

SEHAM, M. (1969). "An American Doctor looks at Eleven Foreign Health Sytems", *Social Science and Medicine* 3: 65-81.

SHELDON, A., BAKER, F., and **MCLAUGHLIN C.** (Eds.), (1970), *Systems and medical care*. (Proceedings of the symposium on Systems and medical Care, Harvard, 1968), Cambridge: MIT Press.

SIDEL, V. and **SIDEL, R.,** (1983). *A Healthy State*. New York: Pantheon.

SIDEL, V. (1980-81) "International Comparisons of Health Services: How? who? why?, *"Policy Studies*, Vol 9, 2, 300-307.

STACEY, M. (1976) *Concepts of Health and Illness: a Working Paper on the concepts and their Relevance for Research social*. Science Research Council.

STACEY, M. (1986) *Concepts of health and illness and the division of labour in health care*. In CURRER C. (supra), 726

STACEY, M., HOMANS, H. (1978) The Sociology of Health and Illness: its present state, future prospects and potential for health research *Sociology*, 12, 19, 281-307.

STOETZEL, J. (1960) La maladie, le malade et le médecin, esquisse d'une analyse psychosociale. *Population*, 15 (4), pp.613-624.

STOETZEL, J. (1963) La conception actuelle de la notion d'attitude en psychologie sociale. *Bulletin de psychologie*, XVI, pp. 1003-1009, Paris.

STOETZEL, J., GIRARD, A., (1973) *Les sondages d'opinion publique*. P.U.F., Paris.

STONE, D. (1980-81) "Obstacles to Learning from Comparative Health Research, *"Policy Studies Journal*, vol 9, 2, 278-285.

STRONG, P. (1975), "Sociological Imperialism and the Profession of Medicine: A Critical Examination of the Thesis of Medical Imperialism", *Social Science and Medicine,* 13 A:199-215.

SUCHMAN, E. A. (1964), "The Comparative Method in Social Research ", *Rural Sociology* 29:123-37.

SZTOMPKA, P. (1986), "The Renaissance of Historical Orientation in Sociology."*International Sociology* 1: 321-37.

SZTOMPKA, P. (1988) "Conceptual frameworks in comparative inquiry: Divergent or convergent?. " *International sociology* " (3), 207-218. t.1: économie, parenté, société, (376 pages); t.2: pouvoir, droit, religion (340 pages) Paris, Les éditions de Minuit.

TAX, B. et al (1984) *Proceedings: Workshop on Lay Culture and Illness Behaviour.* Université de Nijmegen, 346 pages.

TERRIS, M. (1978) "The Three World Systems of Medical Care: Trends and Prospects. *American Journal of Public Health* 68, 11,1125-1131.

TILLY, C. (1984),*Big Structures, Large Processes. Huge Comparisons.* New York: Russell Sage Foundation.

TREIMAN, D. J. (1977). *Occupational Prestige in Comparative Perspective.* New York: Academic Press.

TWADDLE, A. (1986) "*National Roots of health care systems: A comparison of the US, UK and Sweden".* Paper presented at the Congress of the International Sociological Association, New Delhi.

WHITE, K.L. (1968), "Organization and delivery of personal health services: Public policy issues", *The Milbank Memorial Fund Quarterly,* XLVI (1): Part 2, p.228.

WHITE, K.L. et al. (1967), "International comparisons of medical care utilization," *New England Journal of Medicine,* 277: 516-522.

WILLIAMS, R. (1983) Concepts of Health: an analysis of lay logic *Sociology,* 17, 185205

WILLIAMS, R.G.A.(1983) "Concepts of Health: An Analysis of Lay Logic", *Sociology* 17 (2) p.183-205.

WILSFORD, D. (1990) *The politics of health in France and the United States.* Durham NC: Duke University Press.

WILSON, I.D., and **Mc LACHLAN** (eds) (1973) *Health Services Prospects: An International Survey.* Boston: Little Brown

YEN, E. (1986) "The muffling effect of social policy: A comparison of social conflict security systems and their potential in Australia, the United States and Norway. *International sociology* 1 (3), 271-282.

ZELDITCH, M. Jr. (1971) "Intelligible Comparisons" pp. 267-307 in *Comparative Methods in Sociology: Essays on Trends and Applications.* Edited by Ivan Vallier, Berkeley, CA: University of California Press.

SUBJECT INDEX